A BRIEF HISTORY OF QI

ZHANG YU HUAN & KEN ROSE

PARADIGM PUBLICATIONS
Brookline, Massachusetts
2001

A Brief History of Qi

Zhang Yu Huan and Ken Rose

ISBN # 0-912111-63-1

Library of Congress Cataloging-in-Publication Data

Zhang, Yu Huan, 1973-
A brief history of qi / Yu Huan Zhang and Rose Ken.
p. cm.
Includes bibliographical references and index.
ISBN 0-912111-63-1 (alk.)
1. Qi (Chinese philosophy) 2. Philosophy, Taoist. I. Rose, Ken, 1952- II. Title.
B127.C49 Z435 2003
299'.514--dc21

2001006164

Paradigm Publications
44 Linden Street
Brookline, Massachusetts 02445

Printed in the United States of America

Cover design by Laura Shaw Designs

Table of Contents

Acknowledgements

A book about ancient Chinese cultural ideas and artifacts is almost bound to be the result of a collaborative effort. The amount of information that it takes to construct an adequate context for understanding something as fundamental as *qì* can be overwhelming. And once the material is amassed, there is still the even more daunting challenge of coming to understand it. We have been fortunate to have the help of a large number of people in our efforts to meet this challenge. We could not possibly name them all, but there are some who have been uncommonly generous with their time and attention.

Thanks to Nigel Wiseman for reading a relatively early version of the manuscript and offering his comments and encouragement and to Guo Hong Yue for a thoughtful assessment of its strengths and weaknesses. In countless conversations in and out of classes and clinics we have chewed over the ideas that fill the following pages with students, teachers, friends, and loyal adversaries in debate. This is part of the process whereby knowledge can become excellent. Our publishers, Bob Felt and Martha Fielding, honor us with their continued support and cooperation. Without them, this book simply would not have come into being.

Martin Inn has been a steadfast guide on the path of personal understanding and cultivation of *qì* for over thirty years. Students always struggle with the question of how will it ever be possible to repay the gift received from a great teacher. Martin's comment that this is the book he always wanted to write was therefore especially gratifying. Even today it is possible to recognize some of the most basic ideas and sensibilities that appear in the following pages in Martin's *tái jí* class.

Thanks to Tom Kepler for the invitation to visit the Santa Fe Institute and for his thought-provoking discussion that helped us understand ways that the ancient Chinese concept of *qì* might find its way into the vanguard of modern scientific research.

We want to thank Prof. Jiang Yong Guang and the library of the Chengdu University of Traditional Chinese Medicine for access to their research archives. Likewise we want thank Prof. Zhu Jian Ping and the library of the China Academy of Traditional Chinese Medicine for access to their collections and for his guidance and support.

The names mentioned here are just a handful of the people who have helped and encouraged us over the years that we've been working on this book. Despite the help and guidance received, the journey towards understanding *qì* is necessarily a personal one. In the end the questionable decision to write a book about ideas that are hard to grasp and harder still to express was ours alone, as are the necessary omissions and errors that our work, despite our best efforts, no doubt still contains. One of the reasons we present a book like this is, of course, to pass on the received traditions on the subject of *qì*. But another one we acknowledge is to invite the scrutiny of readers in the hopes that they can find and point out our errors.

Zhang Yu Huan and Ken Rose
Chengdu and Berkeley
2001

Preface

THE QUEST FOR UNDERSTANDING ancient Chinese traditions and mysteries has been a continuous theme among Chinese writers throughout recorded history. Thus there has come down to those of us in the current age a rich legacy of literary records that share this theme and bear witness to this enduring quest. Chief among the topics discussed in such works of literature are questions related to *qì*. To the Chinese mind in ages past, qì was a kind of substantial force on which everything depends for sustenance and survival; and it was used as a term in a wide range of discussions on subjects from anatomy to astronomy, and of course medicine. There is *qì* everywhere.

Those familiar with the Chinese literature on the subject will recognize in the current volume, this *Brief History of Qì*, a work that can find an appropriate place in this long literary tradition. Despite the fact that it appears in English, it reflects a deep understanding of the conventions of the Chinese language and Chinese thought. Its rich dependence on classical texts as sources of illustrative material on the manifold aspects of *qì* is evidence of the authors' grasp of the importance of the contextual understanding of this curious Chinese notion, at once simple and complex.

Such a book is frankly rare in the foreign literature on this subject, as non-Chinese scholars and writers have often overlooked the subtleties as well as the grand scheme of traditional Chinese learning. We can see in the pages that follow that the authors have accepted their responsibility for the faithful transmission of Chinese ideas sincerely and have sought to execute it with great devotion. Perhaps it is their personal relationship that lends the authors the immediacy and precision of their insights into how difficult Chinese concepts and words can be rendered into English terms, which appear to this reader to closely convey the sense of the originals. Whatever its origins, we can be grateful for the authors' penetrating appraisal of the roots and branches of this central theme of Chinese literature and life: qì.

Today we stand on the threshold of a new age of scientific synthesis. The treasures of ancient Chinese thought and culture now find their way into the vocabularies and, more importantly, into the theoretical speculation of researchers in a wide range of fields from economics to cosmology to artificial intelligence and life. A growing science of complexity now begins to weave an interconnecting network of theoretical models that can be used to explore and explain a wide spectrum of natural systems.

Lo and behold, the ancient Chinese possessed their own scheme of systematic complexities and correspondences. And, as the authors have faithfully pointed out in the following pages, it all depends on *qì*.

Zhu Jian Ping
China Institute for History of Medicine & Medical Literature
China Academy of Traditional Chinese Medicine
Beijing, China
July 5, 2001

Foreword

Discussion of the Sages with One Single *Qī*

According to written records, Chinese civilization has a history of more than five thousand years. In fact, it should be more than eight thousand years according to recent studies by Chinese scholars. Until today, study and research of ancient civilization and philosophy remain in a more or less chaotic state. modern people who attempt to trace their origins to the ancients often display their ignorance and more resemble than understand barbarians who wore animal skins and drank blood and who danced when the sun rose and sang when the moon appeared. They can differentiate neither gods from ghosts nor truth from illusion. Even the most renowned experts cannot pull themselves out of confusion. Laborious sowing and planting often produces no fruitful harvest.

Ancient philosophy used humble perspectives to explain phenomena. In time some explanations became clear. Some faded away; some were completely abandoned. The theory of one single *qì* comes from the Yin and Zhou periods. It was first raised by Yin Yun of the Warring States period. He was first to assert that *qì* is the basis of material existence. *Qì* is *yuán qì* [original qì]. In Lao Zi's book it is called *dào*. In *Lu's Spring and Autumn Annals*, it is called *tài yī* [great oneness] or *yuán bāo* [original bud]. It is called *tài jí* [ultimate limit] in the *Book of Changes*. In other words, these terms, *tài yī, tài jí,* and *dào* are all synonymous. They refer to the *yuán qì* before the separation of heaven and earth. This *qì* is the material that permeates everything. It "covers heaven and carries the earth, extends in all four directions, and gives rise to the eight extremities. It is so high that it cannot be measured. It folds heaven and earth within it and is possessed of no shape." *Qì* is also a worldview that asserts the whole world came from nothing to something, from chaos to order. From this perspective the *Huai Nan Zi* derived the model of existence of the world: "The *dào* begins with emptiness. Extensive emptiness gives birth to the world. The world gives birth to qì. Qì gives birth to heave and earth. The endowment of the essence of heaven and earth yields yīn and yáng. The concentration of this essence becomes the four seasons. The distribution of essence becomes ten thousand things."

This has become the basic structure of the Chinese worldview for thousands of years. "Heaven and earth mingle their *qì*. The pairing of things gives birth by itself." (Wang Chong). This idea of the *dào* of heaven is the nature of the theory of one single *qì*. All Chinese philosophers follow it. This idea of *qì* is so deep and wide; it binds all Chinese philosophy and culture. This idea covers all of heaven and earth, mankind, nature, the four seasons, emptiness and reality, animals, plants, water and fire, spirits and gods. Who knows how many wise sages and gods have whiled away their days in contemplation of this view of the world. Whole schools of thought, the Daoists and Buddhists, have been absorbed by it. No matter god, sage, wise man, or philosopher, they all obey this idea wholeheartedly and give themselves over to seek its *dào*. From ancient times until today, there is no great opposition to this main theory, even though there has been some variation in the method of practice. Nor does it matter if one is a follower of materialism or idealism. Thus in it we behold the understanding of the divine of the ancient philosophers.

These ancient philosophers believed that the birth, existence, transformation, and disappearance of everything in the world happen under the influence of *qì*. The birth and death of heaven, earth, wind, clouds, thunder, rain, mountains, water, forests, woods, animals, insects, flowers—all are caused by *qì*. The birth, aging, sickness and death of human beings, the persistence of time and the whims of fate, the prosperity and misfortunes of the country, disasters and blessings—all cannot be explained without *qì*. "The birth of ten thousand things all take order from yuán qì." "When heaven and earth mingle their qì, ten thousand things are born. Heaven covers from above, the earth limits from below; and qì steams up from below; qì falls down from above. Ten thousand things are born in between." (Wang Chong).

Thus the understanding of the existence of the whole world comes from the transformation of qì. Therefore, the importance and mysteries of qì have been well established. In *Wang Fu's Qian Fu Lun,* he says:

> *"The function of dào and its virtue does not exceed qì. Dào is the root of qì. Qì is the beginning of dào. It must have root; thus qì is born. It must have beginning; thus transformation is accomplished. The dào acts on things by reaching the divine to become marvelous. This is its charge to arrive at strength to become great. Heaven uses its movements; the earth uses its stillness. The sun uses its light; the moon uses its brightness. The four seasons and five phases, spirits, gods, and people, the myriad manifestations, the changes of good fortune and misfortune, which of these does not result from qì? The inexplicable idea of the virtue of dào. still cannot surpass the idea of qì. Nevertheless, dào is the root of qì. Qì is the function of dào.*

This relationship between the root and the function of Wang Chong left a dispute as to which comes first for later generations. "The surface of the world has no limit, the end of the world is endless." The limitless world is the transformation of great *qì*. There cannot be anything else. It is the same for the creation of heaven. "*Yuán qì* is bright and great, thus it is called bright heaven. Bright heaven is *yuán qì;* it manifests brightness. There is nothing else" (Yang Quan: Chan Fu). The *qì* of *yīn* and *yáng* fulfills the great void. There is nothing outside and there is no gap in between. The appearance of heaven and the shape of the earth are all included in this boundary. However, the transformation of the *qì* of heaven and earth circulates without stopping; it has perpetual life. Thus the life of the ten thousand things is born and grows.

The birth and death of life happens under the influence of *qì;* it transforms emptiness. Emptiness transforms into divinity; divinity transforms into *qì; qì* transforms into blood, blood transforms into shape; shape transforms into infancy; infancy transforms into childhood; childhood transforms into youth; youth transforms into adulthood; adulthood transforms into old age; old age transforms into death; death then turns back to emptiness; emptiness then transforms back to divinity; divinity then transforms back into *qì; qì* then transforms back into things. These transformations are like the chain of rain. It continues without stop. The livelihood and death of the ten thousand things are not issues of self-desire. Even if the ten thousand things have no desire to be born, they must be born. Even if the ten thousand things have no desire to die, they must die. Thus it can be said that birth does not accord to self-desire; death does not accord to self-expectation. Yan Fu says in his *Yuan Qing,* "Subjected to the whole of heaven, earth, humankind, all things, birds and beasts, insects and words, grass and wood, in order to resolve the principle of connection: it all begins with one qì. And it evolves into ten thousand things."

Evidently nothing is not transformed from *qì,* and nothing is not born from *qì.* It is so great that it has no outside, so small that it has no inside, so high that it has no above, so deep that is has no below. It creates heaven and earth and transforms the ten thousand things. It nourishes life. It implements the great *dào.* It threads together rationale and virtue. It is the root and function that can interconnect human nature.

Qì is the mother of things; the mother of things is the mother that gives birth and nourishment to all things. *Qì* includes all things; all appearances are included in it. The *qì* of the country is called "the counting of *qì.*" If the country is divided and its ruler has passed away, it is said, "the counting of *qì* has ended." The *qì* of the general is called "integrity of *qì.*" The *qì* of man is called the "manner of *qì*" or the "qualities of *qì*" The *qì* of heaven is called the "weather of *qì.*" The *qì* of god is called "immortal *qì*" or "spiritual *qì.*" The *qì* of ghosts is called "bewitching *qì*" or "evil *qì.*" The marvel of all things is humanity. Humans are born from *qì.* They receive *qì* from nature. They protect the true *yuán qì.* The body adjusts the *qì* of *yíng* and *wèi.* To be born, one must depend on *qì.* To live, one must depend on *qì.* To grow strong, one must rely on *qì.* Sickness decreases *qì.* Death depletes *qì.* If one does not drink for days or eat for weeks, still one may not die; but one will surely die from not breathing *qì* for less than an hour. It is clear how precious *qì* is.

Zhang Yu Huan and Ken Rose, distinguished scholars of Oriental medicine and philosophy, have worked more than ten years on the subject of *qì.* They consulted thousands of classics to gather and compile material on *qì.* Together they made a thorough inquiry of this idea and wrote *A Brief History of Qì.* This work gives precise explanations of the ontology of *qì,* the transformations of *qì,* and the merging and driving force of *qì* in the fields of ancient Chinese philosophy, literature, art, self-cultivation, medicine, health preservation, and science and technology. It lets Western scholars recognize and understand China. It reveals the apparent chaos and mystery but also the vitality of *qì* so that people can better recognize the indispensable existence of *qì* in the universe.

With the publication of *A Brief History of Qì,* we witness a growing understanding of Oriental culture to which these scholars have made long-lasting contribution to bridge East and West. This achievement should be deeply respected and admired. It conforms to the sentiments of Eastern scholars. I use the tip of my pen to wish that Ken and Yu Huan can harvest more fruit in their research of Eastern culture. When they honored me with a copy of their book, I felt delighted to write this brief foreword.

Professor Chu Cheng Yan
Early Autumn of 2000
At Bu Xi Zhai in Cheng Du
Sichuan, People's Republic of China

「氣」之下話先賢（代序）

褚成炎

中華文明史，據典籍所載，多逾五千，近至專家細考，實則為六千年以上。古人所創之文明以及古老的哲學，相當部份至今仍在潛移默化之中。時人帝王有似「壯齡長」欲延之途，看大限即將，因既朝朝常求，是神仙及煉丹，直至歷代的術士胸懷誘惑，專門研究怎往往使後人既妒，苦耕無果。

古哲用樸素的客觀觀察，闡述事理，從事研究，或已明朗，或已演化，或仍糾纏……。而產生於戰國的「氣一元論」，是我國歷史上第一個提出「氣」是物質的存在。「氣」即元氣，老子書中稱為「道」，《呂氏春秋》稱「太一」，「元氣」，在《易》經稱「太極」。說明「太一」、「太極」、「道」是同意語，指天地未分的「元氣」而言。它既是滋生造化萬物中，覆天載地，廓四方，柝八極，高不可測，包裹天地，稟受無形」的物質。又是宇宙從無到有，從混沌外有

序的一種世界觀（概念二重性）。兩後《淮南子》推出的「道始於虛廓，虛廓生宇宙，宇宙生氣，氣生天地」。「天地之襲精為陰陽，陰陽之專精為四時，四時之散精為萬物（《天文訓》）的宇宙生存模式，成為幾千年來的宇宙生存觀的基本架構。「天地合氣，物偶自生」（王充）的天道自然「氣一元論」更為諸哲遵從。使「氣」這一博大精深，繫系中華哲理、文化，涉天地人倫，草木寒暑，虛空實物，昆蟲禽獸，水火

鬼神的宇宙觀，幾千年來不知消磨了多少明哲仙人，諸子百家，慧道智佛，驚世學者的歲月。神耶，聖耶，哲耶，都表而服其理，身而求其道。古昔而今，唯物唯心之輩，即或棄取視有差，卻大道不悖。可見古哲超人之神悟也！

先哲以為宇宙萬事萬物的產生、存在、變化、消失是受「氣」而化之。天地風雲雷雨，山水林木，禽獸昆蟲，花木，生之亦因氣生，人的生老病死，時乘運

材，國祚興衰，從人生吉凶禍福，無一離乎其「氣」。「萬物自生，皆稟元氣」（王充）。「天地合氣，萬物自生。天覆於上，地偃於下，下氣蒸上，上氣下降，萬物自生其間矣」。對宇宙萬物的生存，視之為氣化所得，這便奠定了「氣」的重要性和令人不易詮釋的神秘性了。王符《潛夫論》云：「道德之用，莫大於氣。道者，氣之根也。氣者，道之使也。必有其根，其氣乃生；必有其使，變化乃成。是故道之為物也，至神以妙；其為

功也，至強以大。天之以動，地之以靜，日之以光，月之以明，四時五行，鬼神人民，億兆醜類，變異吉凶，何非氣然？」人們所見之物類別之後，仍以感受「何非氣然？」數千年來人們難以明狀的「道德」，仍然「莫大於氣」也，且「道者氣之根，氣者道之使」。王氏所言的「根」、「使」關係，給後人遺下難以數說的爭議。

「宇之表無極，宙之端無窮」（張衡《靈憲》）。表無極端無窮的宇宙，是大氣所化，演化而成。天地

然也。元氣雖大，則稱皓天。皓天者，元氣也，皓然而已，無他物也。（楊泉《蠶賦》）陰陽二氣充滿太虛，外無他物，亦無間隙，天之象，地之形，皆其範圍，外無他物，亦無間隙，而天地之氣化，又是流行不息，變不已的。是故生命萬物化生而成焉。

生命的源泉和死亡，是在氣的作用下由虛無而化生的。虛而化神，神而化氣，氣而化血，血而化形，形而化嬰，嬰化童，童化少，少化壯，壯化老，老化死；

死而復化為虛，虛而復化為神，神復化為氣，氣又復化為物。化化不間，由環無窮。萬物生死亦非自欲，萬物非欲生者，不得不生，萬物非欲死而不得不死。可謂生非所欲，死非所期。嚴復《原強》中云：「通天地人物禽獸昆蟲草木以為言，以求其會通之理，始於一氣，演成萬物。」可見氣是無所不化，無所不生，大無其外，小無其內，高無其上，深無其下，成天地，化萬物，育生靈，行大道，貫理德，通人性的根使。

氣是物質。「物質」者，化合萬物之中體也。

氣之無所不包，萬物不盡皆含的。因之，人稱曰「氣數」，國破家亡則云「氣數已盡」，時節之氣為「氣節」，人之氣為「氣派」或「氣質」，天之氣為「氣候」，地之氣為「氣場」或「地氣」，神之氣為「仙氣」或「靈氣」，鬼之氣為「妖氣」或「邪氣」。萬物之生存之理也。上述乃氣，非指自然之氣，還有其它之氣，身、體內營衛之氣。

養陽之氣，強身之氣，壯體之氣，病損之氣，死喪之氣。三日不飲，周身不暖，非比從前，精與氣息多弱之。可見氣之珍也！

著名學者、專家蕭荀老弟，精通各家，得大鏡光生及其同僚將宇宙之組成時千餘載，閱數千萬言，把中華歷代至今有關「氣」的文獻收集整理，編輯闡述，著成《氣之簡史》，使專家學者對「氣」與其奧的古老字中國字，為世界譯者的專著，大凡氣的

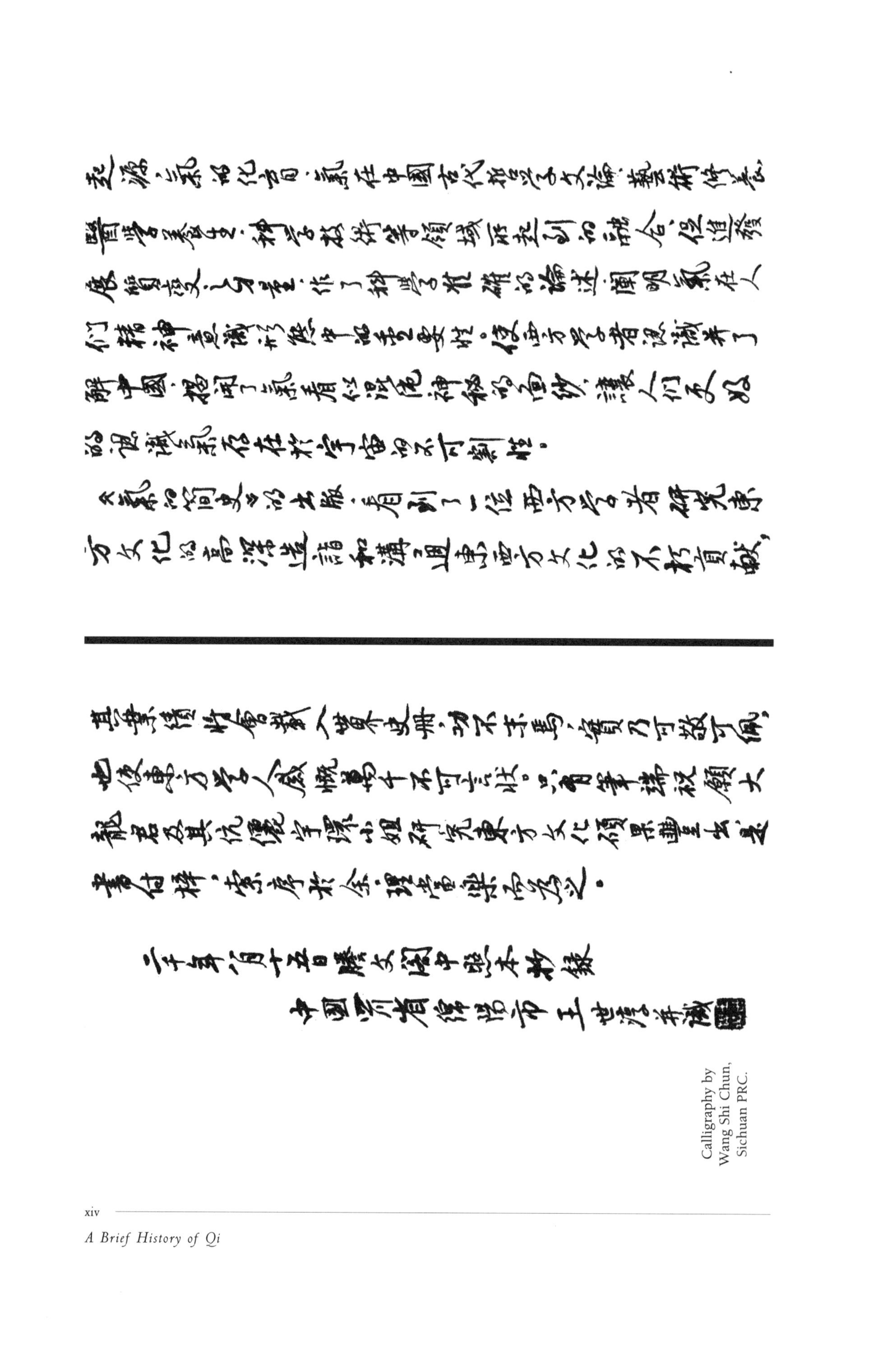

Calligraphy by Wang Shi Chun, Sichuan PRC.

Chapter 1

The Literary Traditions of Qì

The spirit of literature travels far. Contemplated in silence, congealed within a concept, this spirit connects across a thousand years. It can change the expression on a face ten thousand miles away. What a wonderful concept! The principle is: the spirit moves with matter, the same spirit that dwells in the human breast. But it is the qì of the will that moves the crux of all things seen with the eyes or experienced within the body. It all hinges on the pivot of the right word.

The writer of those words was one of China's most renowned literary scholars. Yet did he ever know how far his own congealed spirit would travel? Who knows? It was in the first half of the sixth century C.E. when Liu Xie sat silently beneath the willows and listened to the stream bend by his cottage. He took up his brush and dipped its tip into the small black puddle of ink on his inkstone. But could he have imagined that his words would travel this far? Could it be that as he drew his brush across the rice paper, he felt his spirit touch the pages of the book you now hold in your hands? Does his will not still move here in these things seen with our eyes?

Perhaps he gazed onto the shiny black surface of the ink and it became a magic mirror from which he looks back at our expressions and smiles. What a wonderful concept, indeed! A mystery to which Liu Xie himself gave us a clue: it all hinges on the pivot of the right word. For if we wish to comprehend such mysteries, the right word is *qì*.

Qì is an ancient word. It appears among the oldest texts and fragments of writing yet discovered in China. As all words are, it is the property of those who use it, and it has been used—and abused—for a very long time. Like the Chinese language itself, it has undergone a series of transitions in form and meaning throughout the centuries. As much or more than any other Chinese character, *qì* typifies the problems of translation. It has congealed so much of the spirit of so many Chinese writers—of the Chinese people—that to remove it from its linguistic and literary context is like removing the spirit from the human breast, leaving only the empty form.

Thus we have created this book: a synthetic environment in which this spirit of Chinese thought and action can reside while we work to understand the breadth of its meanings and their intricacies.

We begin with the word itself, a simple glyph we find carved on stones, etched into the walls of ancient temples, and drawn, paradoxically, with careful abandon on countless sheets of rice paper displayed here and there wherever Chinese people live: *Qì*.

Qi calligraphy by Xi Hong Yi

What is this word? What does it really mean?

To establish a firm foundation for understanding its many varied meanings and uses, we turn to the *Great Dictionary of Chinese Characters* (*Hàn Yŭ Dà Zì Diăn*). This eight-volume compendium of Chinese characters is a standard reference for Chinese scholars, comparable in scale and status to the *Oxford English Dictionary*.

In the seemingly endless pages of that book the problem slowly begins to unfold and acquire perspective. On page 2010 in Volume Three, the section devoted to characters composed with the character *qì* (pronounced "chee") begins. Here we find ten ancient forms of this character. Under the heading of the word *qì* itself, there are twenty-three separate definitions given. These numbers only hint at the vast complexity and depth of its meanings.

If we look deeper into the past, searching for a point from which we can say the history of this word begins, everything dissolves into mist. Nothing is clear. There are no boundaries. There are no signs. Only the vaguest impressions come like childhood memories: something brushing against your leg, the wind gently caressing your cheek, thunder almost too far away to hear. We find ourselves in a region that might be described as the unconscious mind of the Chinese people thousands of years ago.

The great Swiss psychoanalyst, Carl Jung, once mused, "Has no one ever stopped to think that when one uses the term 'unconscious mind' that the densest darkness imaginable has thereby been evoked?" The darkness from which the roots of *qì* emerge is dense indeed but it also contains a flash of light, a spark of life. This spark enlivens us and we begin to sort these vague impressions, the rubble of ancient writers, into stacks and piles.

Section One
Etymologies—The Roots of *Qì*

The earliest characters in the Chinese language were pictographic. *Qì* is one such character. When we seek to understand the meanings and uses of these pictographic characters, we must deal with form and content, shape and sound, denotation and connotation, to develop a comprehensive grasp of the meaning. The great Qing Dynasty scholar Duan Yu Cai noted that the character for *qì* originally had the "shape of the rising clouds." In the pictographic system of ancient Chinese writing, this shape was 三. The roots of *qì* are thus firmly planted in an ethereal soil. The ancient character depicted the mists that rise to form the clouds. The character retained this form and meaning until the Zhou Dynasty (1066 B.C.E.–770 B.C.E.) when it was first altered, probably to distinguish it from the character for the number three,

ABOVE: The form of the character *qì* changes over time

sān 三. The first change in shape the character *qì* underwent was the addition of a curved stroke to the left-most end of the top-most of the three lines that composed the original form 气.

The original meaning of the word remained unchanged, however, despite this change in the way it was written. As Duan Yu Cai noted, this original meaning was "cloud *qì*," that is, the rising vapors that gather to form the clouds. Inherent in this oldest meaning is the essence of the mystery of *qì:* it cannot always be seen, but through its changes, its presence can be sensed, experienced, and understood.

The *Great Dictionary of Chinese Characters (Hàn Yǔ Dà Zì Diǎn)* lists three additional meanings for the original character:

1) to give; 2) to beg[1]; 3) to take or to save.

As the character continued to undergo changes in form, the word acquired various meanings. The bottom stroke was eventually curved and a terminal "hook" was added 气, again most probably to distinguish it from other characters.

Along with these changes in its written form, the word developed a series of additional meanings which blended together, deepening its significance. Foremost among these additional meanings was the sense of "breathing in and out."

In *jiǎ gǔ wén* 甲骨文, the ancient language of oracle bone inscriptions, the word did not have this meaning. It meant "to beg for; to arrive"; and "the end." The addition of breathing to the meanings of *qì* came following the Yin and Zhou periods. The Jade Chapter or *Yù Piān* explains *qì* as *xī* 吸 (breathe). In the *Book of Rites (Lǐ Jì)* of the Zhou period, the word *qì* is used to mean breathing in and out.

[1]Today this meaning has been given to a separate word, written *qǐ* 乞 and also pronounced "chee."

Thus, an alternate way of writing the ancient word developed and was used to express this meaning of breath. The character 炁, also pronounced "chee," meant "the *qì* of breathing." This way of writing was primarily used by Daoists and practitioners of various arts related to the cultivation of *qì*. It is found among the characters that comprise the Daoist talisman (at right) from *Tōng Líng Fú*. The purpose of such talismans was to harness the power of the words and display them in effective interrelationship. There are many such talismans, each with a different use. The talisman is meant to protect the body and eliminate desire and evil influences.

There is a phenomenon of the Chinese language known as *tōng jiă zì* which is important to understanding the development of ancient etymologies as well as contemporary meanings. This phenomenon results from the conjunction of the forms, sounds, and meanings in ancient characters. Essentially, when two characters bore a resemblance in shape, sound, and/or meaning, they occasionally came to stand for one another. This process took place between the ancient character *qì* and another word *xì* 餼, pronounced "shee." *Xì* 餼 meant "to give nourishment" or "to give rice." Through the association of these two words, the sense of "nourishing" was added to the overall meaning of *qì*. The character thus went through another of its many transfigurations to include the concept of nourishment. The radical *mĭ* 米 meaning "rice" was added to the inside of the character *qì* 气, depicting that the original notion of a cloud-like vapor now included the idea of the essential nutritive substance.

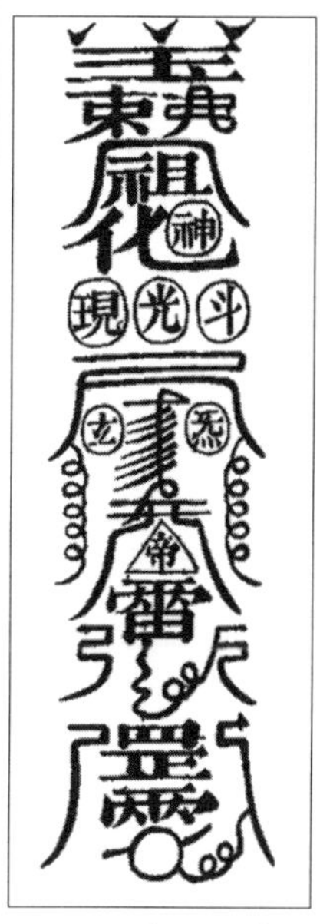

Daoist talisman from *Tōng Líng Fú*

The close relationship between the concept of *qì* and nutrition can also be seen from another perspective. The word in Chinese that means "to eat" is *chī*. It is written 吃. Compare this to the word *qì* 气 and the word *qǐ* 乞. Recall that the character 乞 derived from 气 when the meaning of "begging for food" was abstracted from 气 and given its own form, 乞. These relationships are important in developing a deep understanding of the meaning of *qì*. *Qì* yielded *qǐ* which comes to mean "eat" when the radical for "mouth," *kǒu* 口 is added to it: 吃.

By the 2nd century C.E., the word *qì* had already taken on an elaborate set of meanings related to vitality and life-sustaining substances and processes, while retaining its underlying sense of connective and transformative impetus. In the medical scrolls discovered in Ma Wang Dui in Hunan, Changsha, in southeastern China, the word *qì* appears in several phrases containing such meanings. In the scrolls concerning *yǎng shēng* 養生 or the cultivation of health and long life, we find *jīng qì* 精氣 (essence), *shén qì* 神氣 (spirit), *xuè qì* 血氣 (blood), *qì xuè* 氣血 (*qì* and blood), *zhāo qì* 朝氣 (vitality), and *shí qì* 食氣 (to eat *qì*). A close examination of the meanings of these terms reveals the breadth and depth of the uses that had already become associated with the concept of *qì* before the beginning of the first millennium C.E.

The term *jīng qì* 精氣 refers to the most essential substance from which life begins and on which life depends for its sustenance. The word *jīng* 精 means "essence," "semen," or "ovum." It reflects an ancient understanding of the substance and function of the transmission and continuation of life through sexual reproduction. Ancient medical theorists considered it to be the substance that was transmitted from parents to their offspring at conception. Thus, it can be understood as an ancient expression of the phenomena of genetic transmission that we understand in the modern biological sciences as DNA. As *jīng* is explained in the *Treasured Mirror of Eastern Medicine* (*Dōng Yī Bǎo Jiàn*) by Xu Jun near the end of the Ming Dynasty (1368 C.E–1644 C.E.):

> *The sublime aspect of the Eternal manifests in daily life as jīng* 精. *Thus, it follows the meaning of mǐ* 米 *[rice] and qīng* 青 *[the color of green rice or youth].*

The inclusion of the word *qì* in the phrase *jīng qì* reflects a profound aspect of ancient Chinese medical theory. Ancient theorists understood that for this essence of life to be transmitted, it required an invisible yet functional impetus. This was provided by *qì*.

Shén qì similarly blends *qì* with another of the essential treasures that ancient Chinese medical theorists recognized as indispensable to life itself. *Shén* 神 means "spirit." It reflects the recognition of the ancient doctors that human beings contain a spark of the eternal without which they could not exist. Yet even this eternal flame could not burn without an invisible but essential substance, the breath of life: *qì*. Thus the phrase *shén qì* came to express the medical concept of what can be seen in someone's face and eyes that manifests the innermost vitality, or in other words, spirit.

One of the most significant of the early discoveries of Western medical science was made by William Harvey in the eighteenth century. Prior to Harvey's seminal work in physiology, the West had no clear understanding of the circulation of the blood. By contrast, more than 2000 years ago ancient Chinese medical writers already were well aware of the circulation of blood and of pathways through which it moves. Moreover, they understood that the blood was just one vital substance moving throughout the body.

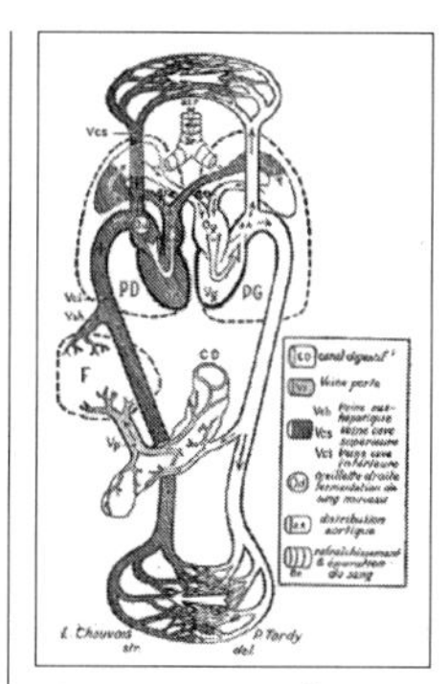

Harvey's circulatory system.

The term *xuè qì* 血氣 was developed to express the essential function of the blood as it coursed through the arteries bringing nutrients to the remotest parts of the body. As with *shén* and *jīng*, *xuè*, blood, could not exist or function without *qì*, its invisible companion.

The relationship between the *qì* and blood was further refined in the term *qì xuè* or "*qì* and blood." This relationship is clearly defined in the ancient medical book known as the *Yellow Emperor's Classic of Internal Medicine* (*Huáng Dì Nèi Jīng*). There, in the *Simple Questions* (*Sù Wèn* 素問) section, it says, "The blood is the mother of the *qì*. The *qì* is the commander of the blood." It was perhaps the recognition of this intimate relationship between *qì* and blood that provided ancient theorists with the understanding necessary to construct a map of the pathways both these essential substances traversed throughout the entire human body. The deceptively simple phrase *qì xuè* contains the gist of this interrelationship.

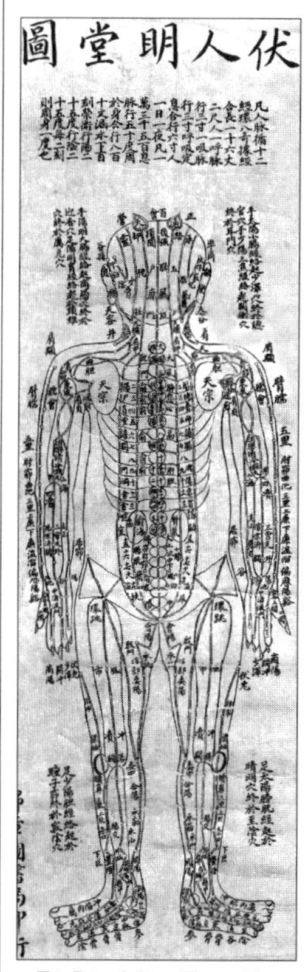

Fú Rén Míng Táng Tú, posterior view. Drawing of the *jīng luò*—pathways of *qì*.

Thus some 2000 years ago the word *qì* had already come to contain a significant set of profound meanings related to the essential substances and functions of the

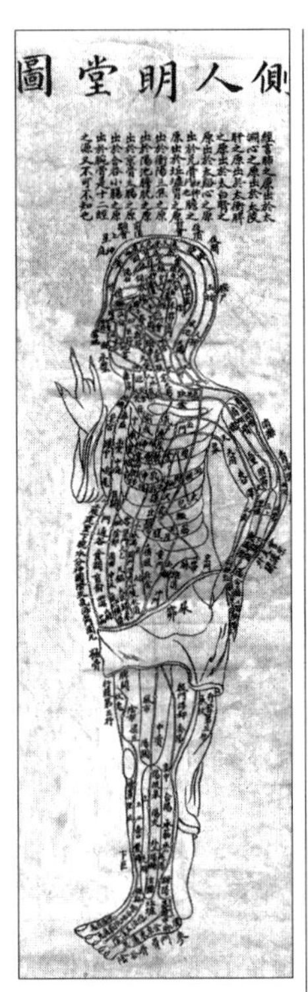

Cè Rén Míng Táng Tú, Drawing of the *jīng luò*—pathways of *qì*.

natural world, the human spirit, and the physiological functions of humankind. To complete this discussion of the roots of the word, we return to the philosophers of ancient China. Before the word took on its meanings in art or medicine, it was endowed with a profound significance by the authors of ancient philosophical texts. We will examine some of China's ancient philosophical classics more thoroughly in the next chapter but here we mention them in the context of etymology.

In the Daoist classic, *Dào Dé Jīng*, the word *qì* appears three times. In Chapter 10, reflecting what has been called his "skeptical mysticism," Lao Zi asks, "In concentrating your *qì* to attain resiliency, can you become like an infant?" In Chapter 42, we get a glimpse of the important relationship between *qì* and the concept of *yīn* and *yáng*: "The ten thousand things bear *yīn* yet embrace *yáng*. Thus their pulsing *qì* unites." In Chapter 55, we see an ancient trace of the practices of Daoist yoga in the phrase, "The heart [mind] directing the *qì* is called 'strength'."

It was not Lao Zi's way to explain himself. What has been called his esoteric magic remains obscure to this day. Yet we can see *qì* moving through the Daoist image of the world, just as we shall see the Daoist influence on the concept of *qì* as it flowed throughout the Chinese cultural imagination.

As noted above, the Daoists even coined a special character to express their unique notion of *qì*, 炁 .

In another of the Daoist classics, *Zhuāng Zǐ*, we find a sentence that sums the universal importance that Daoists imparted to the concept of *qì*: "Throughout all creation there is but one *qì*." This notion is echoed in the writings of Meng Zi (Mencius), the great disciple of Kong Zi (Confucius), who wrote of an all-encompassing *qì* that could be rectified through meditation and the practices of benevolent humanity, education, and rationalism.

By the beginning of the Imperial or Dynastic Era of Chinese history, more than 2000 years ago, the concept of *qì* as the essential connective, transformative, and nutritive component of all creation was firmly established and widely discussed. The word had appeared in numerous philosophical, medical, artistic, and literary works and had carved deep impressions into the Chinese psyche. In the chapters that follow, we will explore further and delve more deeply into the meanings of this word and its vast implications.

Section Two: Definitions

As mentioned, the *Great Dictionary of Chinese Characters* (*Hàn Yŭ Dà Zì Diăn*) gives 23 separate definitions of the word *qì*. We list them here to provide a sense of the range of meanings that the word has accumulated through the centuries.

1. Cloud *qì*. As discussed above, this was the meaning of the word in its generative form, a pictogram of vapor rising to form clouds.
2. The common noun for gases of all kinds. This is clearly an extension of the original meaning to include matter of any kind existing in a gaseous state.
3. Weather, as an example of natural phenomena. Just as the original meaning implied the invisible forces at work in the transformation of water into a vaporous state and then into clouds and once again into liquid form as rain, *qì* took on the meaning of the transformative processes of atmospheric phenomena.
4. Solar terms (ancient divisions of the lunar calendar).
5. Breathing. Again, this is a logical extension of the idea of the gaseous aspect of the atmospheric environment. By association *qì* came to mean the act of breathing. This may also have come about through the process of *tōng jiă zì* mentioned above because *qì* sounds like the word *xī* 吸, meaning "to breathe."
6. Smell, odor, flavor. Once again, we see in the meanings of the word the inclusion of invisible but observable phenomena transmitted through the air. The concept of *qì* developed to include a wide range of effects that could be experienced through breathing, as in the following definition.
7. The verb "to smell."

8. Anger, upset. In Chapter 4 and 7 we discuss the function of *qì* in the various physiological and psychological processes associated with anger as well as emotions generally.
9. A philosophical concept of ancient China. See Chapter 2.
10. A term from Chinese medicine. See Chapter 4.
11. A term in ancient Chinese literary criticism. See Chapter 3.
12. Momentum, particularly referring to spiritual or emotional momentum.
13. Style, habit, particularly a bad habit.
14. Will, also conspiracy, that is, the joining of wills to create action.
15. Spirit, feeling, or temperament.
16. Prevailing custom, general mood, atmosphere.
17. Meteorological phenomena; view.
18. Strength.
19. The various qualities or nature of people or objects.
20. Destiny, fortune, fate, life.
21. Dialect.
22. Suffix, an adjectival additive to words that lends any of the various meanings listed above to other nouns.
23. By association with *qì* 器. Utensil, in common usage with *mǐn* 皿.

As can be seen by the variety of its meanings, the Chinese concept of *qì* is pervasive. We will discuss most of the meanings listed above in the course of the following chapters. In Chapter 7 we focus specifically on the everyday uses of the word, showing that *qì* is not only profoundly philosophical but is also a artistic, literary, and medical concept. It is truly a household word in China.

If nothing else, we hope that the forgoing material has clearly made one point. We have discussed this point with students and colleagues for many years. It is simply that the word *qì* is not easy to translate from Chinese into other languages. Not only does it have a wide variety of distinct meanings, many of these meanings are profound concepts that require years of study and practice to understand and appreciate. Add to this the ability of the Chinese language to have words with variant meanings mean each of those meanings simultaneously, and the difficulties of rendering *qì* into English (or any other non-Chinese language), begin to emerge. If we do not succeed at resolving such difficulties, we hope at least to draw your attention to them so you will develop a clearer and more penetrating understanding.

Section Three: Passages from Ancient Texts

Throughout the text, you will find that we quote extensively from ancient texts to illustrate various aspects of the meaning of *qì*. This section contains a sampling of such quotations. Consider these as *hors d'oeuvres* providing a first taste of the many delicate flavors of *qì*. This word has flowed from the brushes of Chinese writers in every age, and like the seemingly infinite variety of Chinese culinary delicacies, each has its own distinct pleasure. We hope they whet your appetite.

> *Dào* 道 *fills out the physical form. But man cannot locate its existence. It does not reveal its shape. Its voice makes no sound. It exists as implicate order. This is the dào. It has no resting place. It comes to rest in the kind heart. The tranquil heart, the harmonized qì, this is where the dào abides. Thus is the dào: word of mouth cannot pass it on. The eyes cannot behold it. Nor can ears hear it. Its use is the cultivation of the heart to make it upright.*

> *For humankind, if it is lost there will be death; if it is gained there will be life. In action, if it is lost there will be defeat; if it is gained, success. The dào has neither root nor stem, no leaf nor flower. But all ten thousand things are born and grow from it. It is named "dào."*

> *If you concentrate the qì and cross the frontier of the spirit, the ten thousand things can be kept in your heart. But can you concentrate? Can you return to oneness? Can you know the future without divination? Can you come to rest whenever you desire? Can you gain naturally with the help of no*

Guan Zi, Prime Minister of the State of Qi in the Spring & Autumn Period (770–476 B.C.E.)

other? Think it over. Think it over and over and over. Though thinking endlessly still you cannot do it. Spirits and gods can do it, but it is not the power of the spirit or God. It is the power of the essence of qì.

Thus is the life of all humankind as well as heaven endowed with this essence. The earth merely supplements its shape. These two mingle to create humankind. When they are in harmony, all life flows forth. When in disharmony, life is destroyed. Therefore, observe the dào of harmony. But its essence does not appear. Its signs are not revealed through analogies. Let righteousness and peace occupy the chest. Fill the heart 心 *[xīn, mind] with harmony and balance. This will prolong life.*

—Guan Zi

Offering a taste of *qì* is in keeping with an ancient concept of how people could accumulate and cultivate its powers. In ancient writings the ancestors of today's *qì gōng* practitioners were said to "eat *qì*."

Tao Hong Jing

One who eats qì will attain enlightenment [shén míng, spiritual brightness] and prolong life.

—From *Records of Nourishing and Preserving Nature to Prolong Life (Yǎng Xìng Yán Mìng Lù),* by Tao Hong Jing, from the Southern Dynasty (456 C.E.–536 C.E.)

"*To eat qì means breathing deeply and strongly to release the old and receive the new.*

—Wang Chong, *Discussion of Judgments* (*Lùn Héng*) from the Eastern Han period (25 C.E–220 C.E.)

To eat qì is [to be like] the tortoise.

—*The Song of the True Explanation* (*Zhēn Jiě Gē*) by Wang Pin of the Qing Dynasty (1644 C.E–1911 C.E.)

This last quote requires a word or two of explanation. The ancient Chinese venerated the tortoise for its longevity. It can go without eating for months on end. Thus, people revered its vital spirit. They attributed these qualities to the tortoise's supposed ability to eat *qì* instead of food. Because of the tortoise's longevity, it became a symbol of long life and good luck in China. People attributed supernatural abilities to it. Additionally, in prehistoric times tortoise shells were used as artifacts of divination. They were heated until they cracked, and the cracks were then interpreted by shamans and oracular magicians according to the patterns recorded in the *Book of Changes* (*Yì Jīng*) The *Book of History* records that "the tortoise of divinity fell from heaven and was thus used in the practices of divination." Moreover, tortoises and turtles may be used as ingredients in specific herbal formulas. Their chief medicinal function is to nourish the *yīn* and essence to increase the body's capacity for generating *qì*. (See Chapter 4 for a discussion of *yīn* and essence, and their relationship with *qì*.)

Drawing of the Daoist immortal Huang An, from the Ming Dynasty text *Liè Xiān Quán Zhuàn*.

Section Four: Selections from Modern Writers

Following the example of their ancestors, modern Chinese writers have concerned themselves with explications of the nature and functions of *qì*. Here again is just a sampling of the works of several exponents of modern Chinese letters.

> *Chinese medicine is mainly based on transformations of ch'i. You must use the cultivation of ch'i for tuberculosis, or it cannot be cured. Therefore, it is easier to cure tuberculosis with Chinese traditional medicine than with Western methods.*
>
> —*Cheng Tzu's Thirteen Treatises on T'ai Chi Ch'uan* by Cheng Man Ching, translated by Benjamin Peng Jeng Lo and Martin Inn.

In his 1936 book entitled *My Country, My People*, the noted writer Lin Yu Tang touched on the pivotal role of *qì* in the philosophy of Daoism:

Last of all, it [Daoism] offered a formula for bodily hygiene, chiefly by deep-breathing, leading to immortality by ascent to heaven on the back of a stork. Its most useful word was ch'i (air? breath? spirit?) which, being invisible, was most susceptible of "mystic" handling. The application of this ch'i was practically universal, from the rays of a comet to boxing, deep-breathing and sexual union, which was sedulously practiced as an art (with preference for virgins) in the cause of prolongation of life. Taoism was, in short, the Chinese attempt to discover the mysteries of nature.

The power of *qì* was not overlooked by China's Communist leaders. The following story is from the August 26, 1959 edition of the *Guang Ming Daily* (*Guāng Míng Rì Bào*).

We usually say, "The qì should be relentlessly promoted." This is very important not only to the people's revolutionary activities but to one's personal work. Qì means shì qì 士氣, that is, morale, which is the spiritual side of the warrior. In battle a warrior's appearance is the deciding factor. Brave or timid; success or loss. We all know the historic story of the battle at the River Fei. The Qin general, Fu Jian, commanded an advanced and superior military force. But he was imperious and arrogant. Xie Xuan, the general of the State of Jin, managed his army rigorously and strictly. Thus, he could gain victories with a small military force. Xie Xuan sent agents to undermine the [morale of] Qin's encampment. They had orders to shout, "Fu Jian has already lost." This loud shouting shook the morale of the Qin army and they became disordered. In the ensuing battle they were badly beaten. This type of tactic attacks the heart and destroys the enemy's shì qì.

Indeed, the question of *qì* has continued to occupy the minds of some of China's leading academics until the present day. Here is a passage from a 1996 book entitled *Aura of Life* (*Shēng Mìng Dé Guāng Huán*) in which Tang Zheng Xu, Chairman of the Department of Literature of Sichuan Union University, discusses the difficulties of literature for native Chinese scholars:

Why is it so difficult to penetrate more deeply into the research of ancient literature? We believe the crux of the problem is that most books examining ancient literature lack the spirit of seeking the root by tracing its origins. They satisfy themselves with descriptions of phenomena. This problem is most clearly revealed at the most difficult junctures such as questions concerning qì 氣, shén 神 (spirit), fēng gǔ 風骨 [strength of character or style], yùn 韵 [rhythm, charming], wèi 味 [flavor], wù 悟 [understanding], and so forth. Most research is conducted to explore what such concepts are without going deeper to understand, why? For example, people are fond of explaining what wén qì 文氣 [literary qì] is, and what fēng gǔ 風骨 is. But they are not fond of looking into why such concepts arose in ancient China. Why are ancient Chinese literary works so carefully focused on wén qì and the charm of qì? The basic reason is the special worldview and the life consciousness of the ancient Chinese. They believed that the whole universe was created by qì. Heaven and earth are unified by this entity, qì.

Professor Tang seems to agree with the opinion his predecessor, Liu Xie, whom we quoted at the beginning of this chapter:

The history of [different parts of] the world bears a striking resemblance. Even separated by a thousand years or ten thousand miles, people everywhere have realized that qì is the original substance from which the universe formed. It is the true origin of life.

In the next section we take a look at concepts from other parts of the ancient and contemporary worlds that demonstrate the validity of such arguments, which have indeed spanned thousands of years and traveled tens of thousands miles.

Section Five: Concepts in Other Cultures that Correlate with *Qì*

The Chinese were not alone among the ancient peoples who perceived the natural world as the confluence of primeval forces. Nor, as indicated by the rapid growth of traditional Chinese medicine in the West, are they the only people in the contemporary world who find value and benefits in understanding the world as transformations of *qì*. In fact, a survey of concepts in either the ancient or modern worlds that approximate the meanings of *qì* would require a book of its own.

The ancient Hindus wrote of *prana*, the invisible "breath of life" that they cultivated through Yoga. Ancient Greeks described a concept which in several important aspects parallels the Chinese notion of *qì* with the word "pneuma." Like the Chinese *qì*, this Greek word is often translated into English as "breath"—with similarly misleading results. The Greek pneuma, like the Chinese concept of *qì*, was a complex idea that blended spiritual and material aspects of the vital essence of life into a comprehensive description of that without which life itself could not exist.

Heraclitus

The great Greek philosopher Heraclitus defined a school of thought in which the concept of pneuma played a central role. This is expressed by the famous phrase, "everything is in flux." Also like *qì* in ancient China, pneuma was an important concept in ancient Greek medicine. It too was the substance with which people filled their lungs ("pneumon" in Greek). But like its Chinese counterpart, the Greek pneuma represented an even more vital substance. It took on the meaning of the breath of life, breathed into mortals by the gods. This substance provided the medium whereby divine "inspiration" (literally "breathing in") took place. And, like *qì* in China, pneuma came to be understood as the primary connective substance by which the organic interrelationships of all creation were established and maintained.

The concept of *qì*, particularly with respect to its intimate relationship to *yīn* and *yáng*, has another close parallel in ancient Greek philosophy. The Greek philosopher Democritus postulated the existence of indivisible, elemental increments of matter from which all things were composed. These "atoms" (from the Greek meaning "that which cannot be cut," *i.e.*, the irreducible) served as the basis of the centuries-long search in Western sciences for the elemental particle, a search that continues today.

陽極陰極

tài jí tú

The concept of indivisibility is contained in the Chinese counterpart of the atom, depicted since ancient times by the familiar diagram of *yīn* and *yáng* called *tài jí tú*.

Like the ancient Greek atom, the *tài jí* diagram is a description of that from which all matter was made. The indivisible interpenetration of *yīn* and *yáng* gave rise to the primordial pulsing of *qì*. According to their ancient meanings, neither the atom nor *yīn* and *yáng* can be divided. Having split the atom, modern physicists now look ever more deeply into the fabric of the universe seeking a repository of this principle of indivisibility.

Another tradition from the ancient world that elucidates a concept remarkably similar to the Chinese concept of *qì* is found in the Hebrew Kabbalah. In fact, many of the essential philosophical concepts discussed in the following chapter closely conform to Kabbalistic beliefs. There are, of course, distinct differences as well. Here we must note that the Kabbalah is neither easily accessible, nor is it a field that we have extensively studied ourselves. For the comparisons and contrasts between the ancient Chinese concepts of *qì* and what we find as compelling parallels with ideas from the Kabbalah, we have relied on the texts that students of the Kabbalah have chosen to best represent ancient Hebrew mysticism. The material that follows provides another perspective from which the concept of *qì* can be perceived and appreciated.

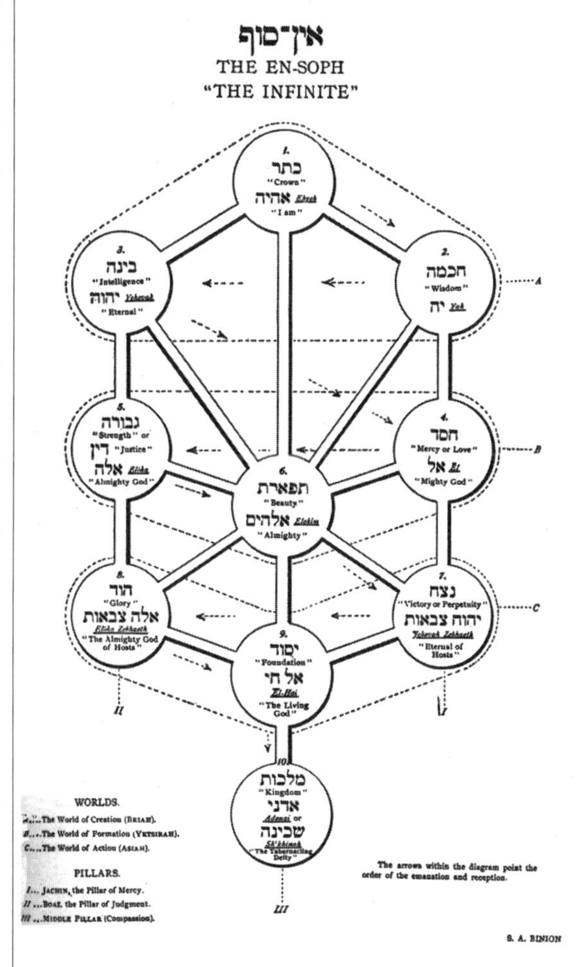

According to Dr. David Sheinkin, a psychiatrist and theologian, writing in *Path of the Kabbalah,* Kabbalists "believe the Bible is actually telling us something about the circuitry of the universe—how it is 'wired'—so that a knowledgeable individual could learn how to manipulate *the very forces of creation* [emphasis added]." Dr. Sheinkin describes the Kabbalistic understanding of the "identity" of God as "the undifferentiated and trans-infinite nature of the *Ain Sof.*" This concept would be a perfectly acceptable translation of the Chinese term *wú jí* 無 極 or "limitlessness," which is used to describe the state of the universe before the initial act of creation.

In one of several remarks that resonate harmoniously with Chinese metaphysics, Dr. Sheinkin explains:

> *Everything that exists does so because God originally created it and because God's creative flow continues to sustain that object. This concept is a primary tenet of Jewish philosophy and is central to the Kabbalah. In the same way this esoteric system teaches that a bridge connects man and God, and continues to exist in the creative flow between them. The same creative force that was utilized in creating the universe is utilized in sustaining it at every instant. If we can attune ourselves to this creative force, we have a bridge—a pathway—between ourselves and God. Therefore, if we truly understand the divine flow described in Genesis, we possess knowledge to bring ourselves closer to the Holy One.*

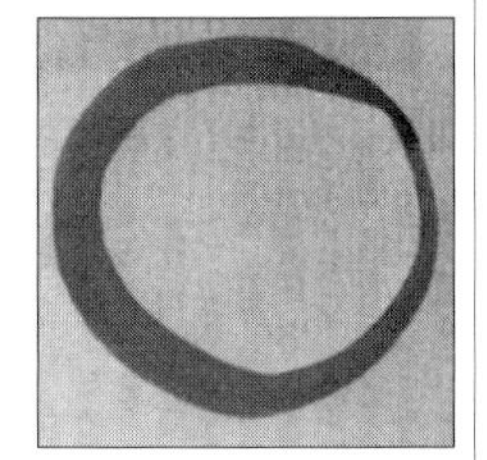

wú jí 無極

This language so closely parallels comparable ideas found in ancient Daoist texts concerning the nature and cultivation of *qì* as to be quite striking. Phrases such as "creative force" and "divine flow" could be inserted into these ancient Chinese texts in place of the concept of *qì* with virtually no displacement of the original Chinese meaning. Dr. Sheinkin's expressions in describing the Kabbalistic interpretation of God and the creative force that continuously supplies the universe with its interconnected patterns of "divine flow" read almost like translations of Daoist texts.

Compare the opening lines from Lao Zi's *Dào Dé Jīng:*

The dào that can be spoken
Is not the eternal dào.
The name that can be named
Is not the eternal name.

with these lines from *The Path of the Kabbalah:*

> *Transcendent of human language, there is literally nothing we can meaningfully say about Ain Sof. One cannot start a sentence with the word "God"*

and complete it with anything meaningful. For example, we cannot meaningfully say "God is good" because God totally transcends our limited concepts of good and evil. God is without limits. The moment we declare, "God is..." the sentence loses its meaning, because God is without limits.

The concept of a limitless source of all creation which gives rise to an omnipresent cosmic creative flow is inherent in the ancient traditions of both Hebrew and Chinese mysticism. It is far more than coincidence that the name of God never appears in the Torah. The namelessness and unknowability of the ultimate source of all creation is a fundamentally important aspect of both systems of belief and practice. A passage from the *Dào Dé Jīng* subsequent to that quoted above underscores this parallel: "That which has no name is the origin of heaven and earth." As will become clearer in the following chapter, the concern of the Daoists was to achieve awareness of the cosmic creative force that endows all creation with its very existence and to develop methods of accumulating, cultivating, and refining this essential force of life.

Dr. Sheinkin also makes it unmistakably clear that the Kabbalistic tradition is not simply a body of ideas or beliefs but is rather a guide for those who seek to cultivate and refine their relationship with the profound forces described in the Bible, particularly to connect with and draw closer to God. Again we see a definite parallel with the teachings of the Daoists who sought not merely to enumerate a hierarchy of universal principles but to establish a path that could be followed to harmonize with the great *dào* of nature.

Jewish sages have long taught that creation was not an event that happened once in the unimaginable past and then ended. They have instead argued that the universe exists at this very moment—and at every moment—because the Holy One wills that celestial flow to continue. God's inconceivable energy creates the cosmos anew at every tiniest billionth-to-billionth of a second. If God for one instant withdrew His Being from our universe, everything—from the greatest galaxies to the smallest subatomic particles—would cease to exist. All would revert back to the Ain Sof.

From this compelling concept it follows that the creative flow described in Chapter One of *Genesis* did not end in the distant past but continues at this moment. Kabbalists declare that the bridge between God and man still exists in the creative flow that emanates from *Ain Sof* at every instant. Therefore, by attuning ourselves to this heavenly flow, we can bring ourselves closer to God. The forces that link us to God are the channels we must cross to reach Him. This is the basic concept to bear in mind. Thus, there is something in the narrative of the first seven days of creation that will explain the nature of these channels to be crossed. From this perspective, the entire account of creation is a meditative device; it provides a spiritual message for connecting these forces. Indeed, Kabbalists indicate that we can link ourselves meditatively to these celestial forces; that each description in the text radiates a specific detail pertaining to meditation.

In the sense just mentioned, such descriptions of "creative force" and "divine flow" could be inserted into various Daoist texts (as well as other ancient Chinese writings) in place of the word *qì* with no substantial deviation from the meaning of the original. So could a person who understands the nature of *qì* freely replace this ancient Chinese idea for phrases in the preceding quotations without disturbing their meaning in the slightest way. We recognize that such concepts are profound philosophical and religious notions that have captivated the imaginations of some of the world's greatest minds for millennia. Thus we do not presume to explain them here, only to take note of these striking similarities between two ancient ways of thinking and talking about the mysteries of creation.

Sir Isaac Newton

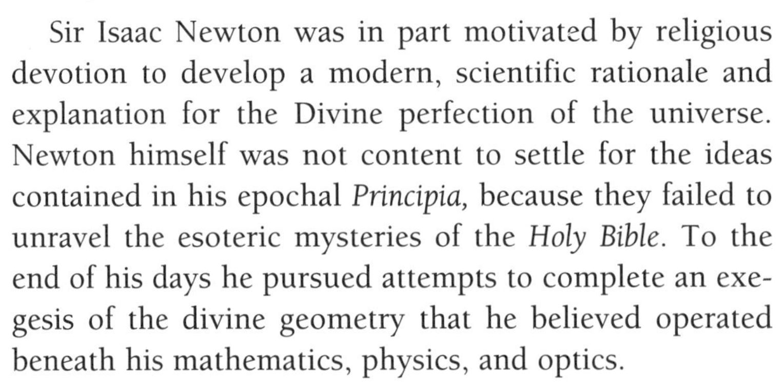

Sir Isaac Newton was in part motivated by religious devotion to develop a modern, scientific rationale and explanation for the Divine perfection of the universe. Newton himself was not content to settle for the ideas contained in his epochal *Principia,* because they failed to unravel the esoteric mysteries of the *Holy Bible.* To the end of his days he pursued attempts to complete an exegesis of the divine geometry that he believed operated beneath his mathematics, physics, and optics.

So too has the concept of *qì* filled the imagination of Chinese scholars and scientists for thousands of years. We will return again to the theme of comparisons and contrasts between Western and Eastern notions that are equivalent or strikingly different that the concept of *qì*. Before we leave the subject for the present, however, we will note a classic example of cross-cultural misunderstanding that relates to the apprehension of *qì* among Western scholars.

The French philosopher Henri Bergson used the phrase *elan vital* to describe his notion of the essence of mankind's vitality. This phrase was also applied by early French translators of Chinese medical texts to the word *qì*, which they translated as *energie* because they correctly understood the Chinese idea to refer to the vital, motivating force of life. However, Bergson's concept is distinctly different from what a well-educated student of Chinese culture understands by the word *qì*. This is not to suggest that it is an absolutely incorrect translation of *qì* into French. That is not the point. The point is that in the wake of this one episode of the saga of the Western reception (and therefore translation) of Chinese language and culture, the modern scientific notion of energy has been substituted for the Chinese sensibilities that inhabit the word qì.

The great danger in translation is not "no understanding." In fact, "no understanding" is the necessary starting point of all translation. At first, we know nothing of foreign words and meanings. As we develop a glossary that permits identification of equivalent concepts, we gather knowledge and experience—not just of the linguistic but also the broader cultural dimensions of both the source and target languages. The great danger to which we refer is the acceptance of meanings and understandings as equivalent which simply are not. To misidentify two things as identical which are not results in catastrophic failures of translation. It is an even more treacherous problem when two things which are merely similar are construed to be identical.

There is, indeed, some similarity between the Bergsonian notion of *elan vital* and the Chinese concept of *qì*. But when they are assumed to be equivalent—identical—one has succumbed to this grave danger. A deep understanding of *qì* is often difficult to develop. It is only made more difficult by the assumption that it is the same as concepts or words from other cultures and other languages when it merely resembles them in some ways and to certain extents.

Here again, we come to the rationale or argument for this book. If we sincerely wish to know what *qì* is, we must set aside assumptions and examine the ideas that have grown around it for the past several thousand years from their roots upward. Thus, we proceed to the development of the concept of *qì* as it is reflected in the writings of Chinese philosophers from the past 2500 years or more. From there we follow the word through its many incarnations in the fields of art, medicine, *qì gōng,* martial arts, and finally back to the realm of daily life.

At each step of the way we are attentive to the parallels, comparisons, and distinctive contrasts that exist between *qì* and similar concepts from other cultural traditions. Here and there we stop to examine some of these parallels. Far more often however, we simply notice them and pass them by, keeping our attention focused on where we want to go. That is to a place where there can be a meeting of minds with respect to the meaning of *qì*.

In the deepest sense, no one can tell anyone else the ultimate or complete meaning of *qì*. According to ancient Chinese traditions, such an understanding is only achieved through individual contemplation. Hence we travel together through this antique landscape of esoteric wonders. We can only give the same advice that we have so often received from our teachers as we forge ahead with eyes wide open: relax and do not resist; but do not let go. We're going for a little ride.

Huang Ren Lan, a Daoist immortal, rides on a dragon.
From the Ming Dynasty text *Liè Xiān Quán Zhuàn*.

Chapter 2

The Qì of the Philosophers

Throughout all creation, there is but one qì.

—Zhuang Zi, (c.400 B.C.E.)

Chinese philosophy begins with observation of the natural world. "All things are stirring about," said the venerable sage of Daoism, Lao Zi, "I watch their cycle." This observation naturally gave rise to attempts to describe what had been observed and throughout Chinese history these descriptions have always contained the concept *qì*. Philosophers throughout China's many ages and dynasties have contributed to the complex of meanings that attend to this word. Thus, our next step traces the path of *qì* through Chinese philosophy.

On page 2012 of Volume Three of *The Great Dictionary of Chinese Characters (Hàn Yŭ Dà Zì Diăn)* we find the ninth definition of the word *qì:* "A philosophical concept of ancient China." Here we translate the entire ninth definition to provide a sense of the significance that Chinese philosophers have attached to the word.

1. Näive materialists believed qì to be the most basic material substance forming everything in the universe. It was named yuán qì or "original qì." It is also known as "yīn qì and yáng qì." Part One of Appended

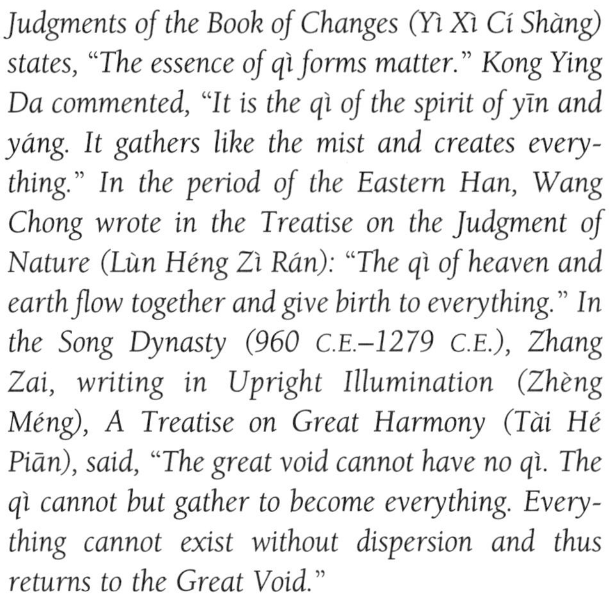
Judgments of the Book of Changes (Yì Xì Cí Shàng) states, "The essence of qì forms matter." Kong Ying Da commented, "It is the qì of the spirit of yīn and yáng. It gathers like the mist and creates everything." In the period of the Eastern Han, Wang Chong wrote in the Treatise on the Judgment of Nature (Lùn Héng Zì Rán): "The qì of heaven and earth flow together and give birth to everything." In the Song Dynasty (960 C.E.–1279 C.E.), Zhang Zai, writing in Upright Illumination (Zhèng Méng), A Treatise on Great Harmony (Tài Hé Piān), said, "The great void cannot have no qì. The qì cannot but gather to become everything. Everything cannot exist without dispersion and thus returns to the Great Void."

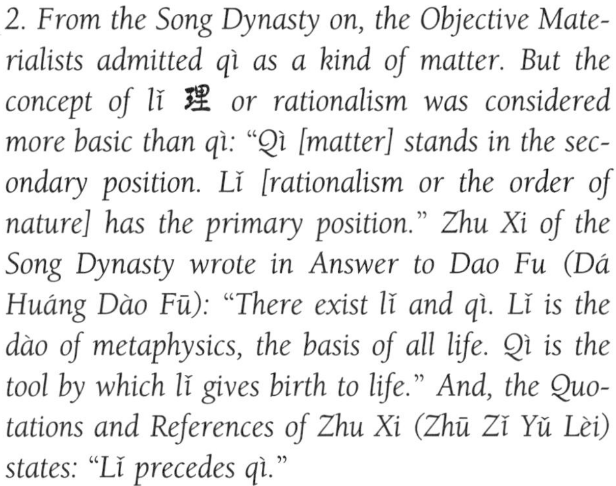
2. From the Song Dynasty on, the Objective Materialists admitted qì as a kind of matter. But the concept of lǐ 理 *or rationalism was considered more basic than qì: "Qì [matter] stands in the secondary position. Lǐ [rationalism or the order of nature] has the primary position." Zhu Xi of the Song Dynasty wrote in Answer to Dao Fu (Dá Huáng Dào Fū): "There exist lǐ and qì. Lǐ is the dào of metaphysics, the basis of all life. Qì is the tool by which lǐ gives birth to life." And, the Quotations and References of Zhu Xi (Zhū Zǐ Yǔ Lèi) states: "Lǐ precedes qì."*

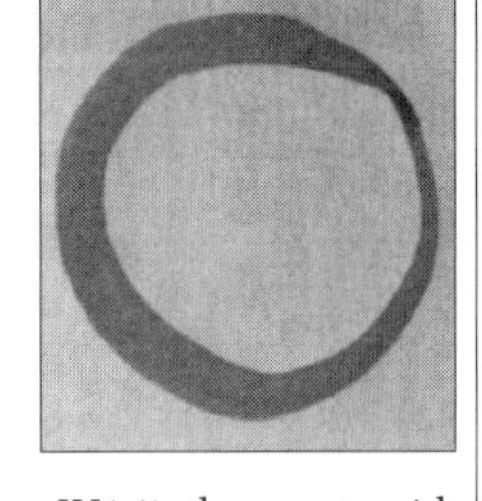
Wú jí, the great void

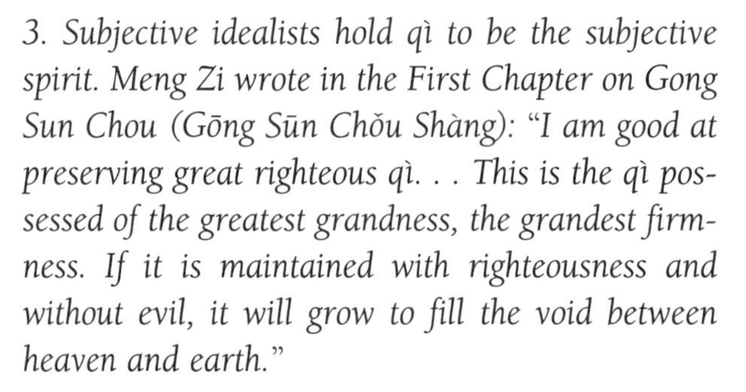
3. Subjective idealists hold qì to be the subjective spirit. Meng Zi wrote in the First Chapter on Gong Sun Chou (Gōng Sūn Chǒu Shàng): "I am good at preserving great righteous qì. . . This is the qì possessed of the greatest grandness, the grandest firmness. If it is maintained with righteousness and without evil, it will grow to fill the void between heaven and earth."

Philosophers in China have used *qì* to describe and explain virtually every phenomena. Its presence signifies and motivates life. Its absence is death. Although invisible, its traces can be seen throughout all existence. We return to the trail of *qì*, again in the ancient Chinese explanations of creation and existence.

Section One: The Role of *Qì* in Ancient Cosmology and Ontology

"In the beginning was the word," according to the *Book of Genesis*. To the ancient Chinese mind, the world begins with *qì*. In the Chinese version of the creation of the universe, the primordial word is *qì*. However, it is not the same *qì* that fills the space between heaven and earth today. It was a substance that is strikingly similar to the state of matter that contemporary astrophysicists and cosmologists postulate to exist within the core of neutron stars where the protons and electrons of a star's atoms have been collapsed by unimaginable gravitational force, compressed into neutron soup. Perhaps it is like the state of the "universe" prior to the Big Bang that gave birth to the universe we observe today. The Chinese name of this mysterious substance is simply *yuán qì* 元氣, "original *qì*."

A vivid description of *yuán qì* can be found the Chinese myth of Pan Gu. It is a story that has been told for hundreds if not thousands of years, a creation myth that in many ways parallels those found in the folklore of cultures everywhere. The story goes that before the universe came to be there existed only a giant egg. Everything that has ever been or ever will be was compacted inside this giant egg, along with a giant named Pan Gu. Nothing was differentiated. All things, all matter, all space, all energies were squeezed together into a formless substance within the egg. This undifferentiated substance was *yuán qì*.

Pan Gu

In Chinese philosophy, this is the state of existence prior to the separation of *yīn* and *yáng*. Then, according to the myth, without explanation this primordial egg cracked, allowing Pan Gu, the giant who lived within it, to escape. Thus, the universe was created through the birth of the giant. Because Pan Gu escaped the broken cosmic egg, the *yuán qì* flowed out. As it issued from the egg, the *yuán qì* differentiated, dividing into two fundamental substances. The clear and light (*yáng*) portions rose to form heaven. The turbid and dense (*yīn*) parts gathered and sank to become the earth.

This separation of *yuán qì* into two essential phenomena gives rise to the differentiation of *yīn* and *yáng* that characterizes all creation and existence. According to the primary dialectics of ancient Chinese thought, everything we experience results from the interplay of these two complimentary opposites. The clearest and simplest explanation of *qì* is that it is the interchange of *yīn* and *yáng*. However, such simplicity leaves little with which to fashion a useful comprehension. Thus, we press forward in search of clarification for concepts that are indeed deceptively simple.

What is clear and comprehensible, however, is that since ancient times the Chinese have conceived of *qì* as something indispensable to all existence, the fundamental substance from which all things rise and upon which everything depends for survival. This is reflected in many common Chinese expressions. To "have *qì*" is to be alive. The dead are those "without *qì*."

Tài jí tú

The notion that the world begins with *qì* developed in the writings of Daoists. In Section Three we more fully explore the content of these writings. But, if there were only one passage from the *Dào Dé Jīng* 道德經 that could be included in this discussion of *qì* and cosmology, it would be the mathematical reduction of the essence of Daoist metaphysics. It states simply, if more than a little obtusely:

Dào gives birth to One.
One gives birth to Two.
Two gives birth to Three.
Three gives birth to Ten Thousand Things.

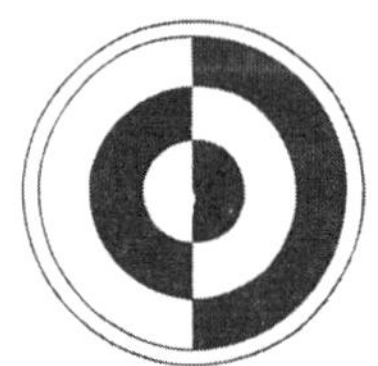

This apparently simplistic mathematical reduction lies at the root of a comprehensive system of metaphysics. We will return to this phrase again. For now we note that in the most abstract terms the *Dào Dé Jīng* records the gist of relationships between the Great Void, that which precedes creation, the *dào*, *yīn yáng*, *qì*, and every ensuing aspect of creation. The Great Void exists prior to the *dào*. The Oneness of *dào* manifests in or "gives birth to" *yīn* and *yáng*, the "Two." *Yīn* and *yáng* give birth to *qì* and thus they are "Three." The eternal interplay between *yīn* and *yáng*, in other words *qì*, gives birth to the Ten Thousand Things—that is, everything.

If we interpret the *dào* as the great river of all existence, then we can glimpse the relationship between *qì* and *dào*: *qì* is the fact and substance of this river's flow.

Section Two: *Qì* in the Explanations of Natural Phenomena and as the Basis of Social Structures

The philosophical discussion of *qì* probably begins in two works known as *The Annals of Spring and Autumn (Zuǒ Zhuàn)* and *Words from [Various] Countries (Guó Yǔ). The Annals of Spring and Autumn* is the historical record of the Spring and Autumn period (770 B.C.E–476 B.C.E) and is sometimes referred to as the *Biographies of Spring and Autumn.* In later ages textual research and documentation set the actual date of this book to the middle of the Warring States period (475 B.C.E.–221 B.C.E.). In it there is an entry which poses the theory of "six *qì*."

> *Heaven possesses six qì. These give birth to the five flavors and manifest in the five colors. Their portent can be heard in the five musical tones. If replete, these six qì will result in disease.*[1] *They are known as: yīn, yáng, wind, rain, gloom [darkness], and brightness. They are classified according to the four seasons and arranged in the order of the five divisions.*[2]

---

[1] Cf. Chapter 4, Section 5.

[2] Regarding the five divisions (*wǔ yùn*) 五運 : The ancient Chinese applied the theory of the five phases (metal, water, wood, fire, and earth) to the four seasons according to the following system. The ancient lunar calendar divided 360 days into five equal periods of 72 days each. Each 72-day period constituted one division. The Wood phase correlated with Spring. Fire was the phase of Summer. Metal was the Autumn phase, and Water the phase of Winter. Each season consisted of 90 days, the last 18 days of which belonged to the earth element. Thus, each year consisted of five equal divisions that related the five phases to the four seasons.

If this order is transgressed, there will be disaster. Replete yīn results in diseases of the cold. Replete yáng causes heat diseases. A superabundance of wind afflicts the limbs. A superabundance of rain results in abdominal illness. A superabundance of darkness causes diseases of the mind. A superabundance of brightness injures the heart.

Here we see an early source of the complex relationships between *qì* in its six manifestations, the five phases, five colors, five flavors, five sounds, and the seasons. In traditional accounts, a fifth season, known as Long Summer, was added to accord with the scheme of the five phases. Such a scheme established *qì* as the fundamental descriptor of natural phenomena and laid the intellectual framework for using this model of the natural world as the foundation of ideal social structures.

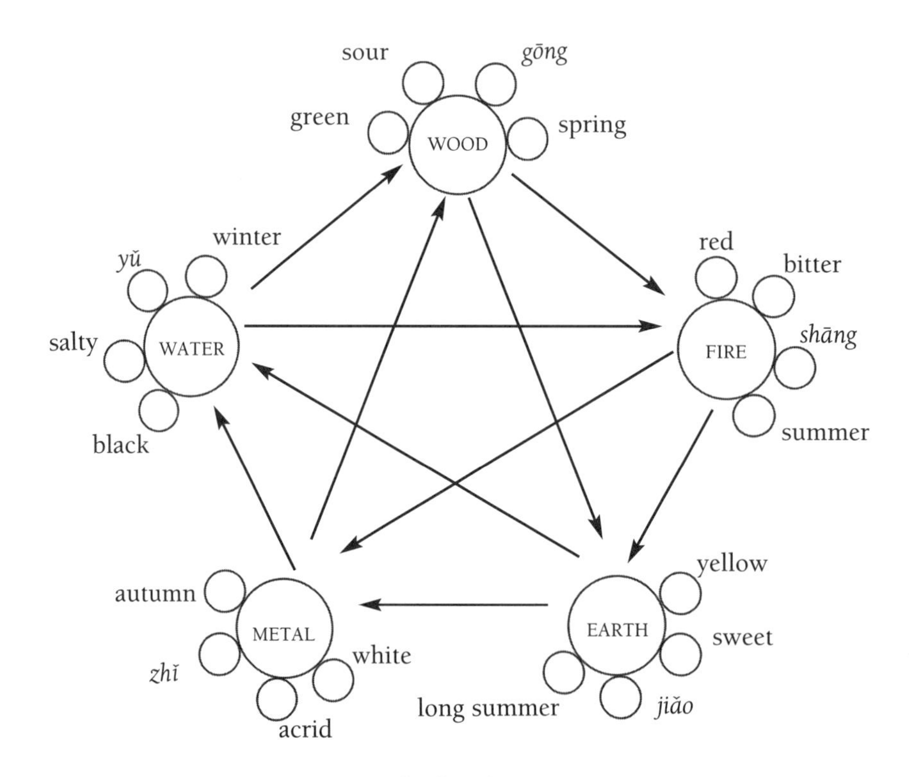

The five phases

The *Guó Yǔ* contains further early evidence of this approach to ordering natural phenomena and human civilization. *Guó Yǔ* is the earliest record of the eight historic nation states that existed in the geographic area that was unified into China by the first Qin Emperor. The work consists of a total of twenty-one volumes that record the "words of [these eight different] countries," which is precisely the meaning of the title. The attributed author was Zuo Qiu Ming who lived in the Spring and Autumn Period, although to date, there is still no conclusive evidence to substantiate this traditional attribution.

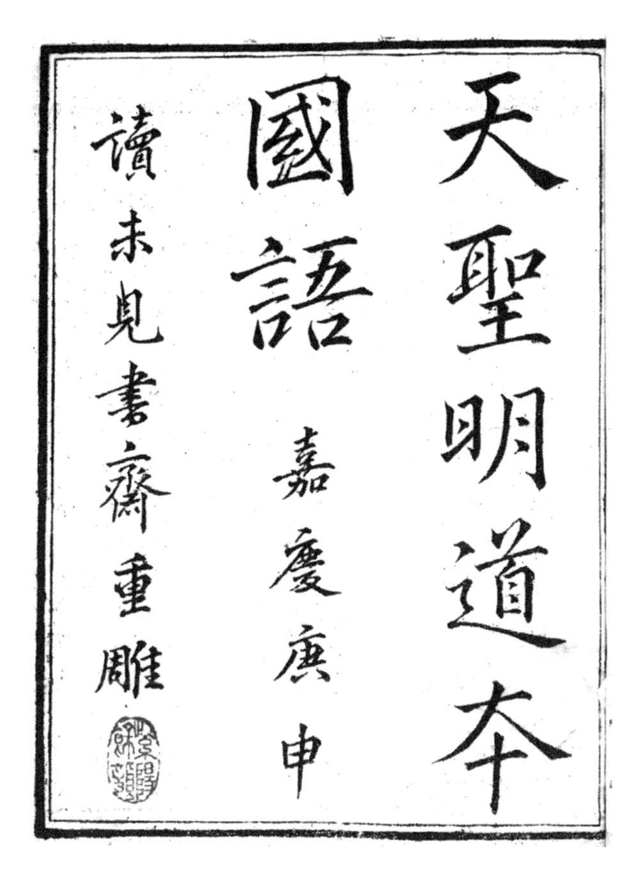
天聖明道本
國語
嘉慶庚申
讀未見書齋重雕

The book *Guó Yǔ*.

As in the foregoing quotation from the *Zuǒ Zhuàn,* the *Guó Yǔ* records evidence of *qì* as having been considered "the *qì* of heaven and earth" and "the *qì* of *yīn* and *yáng*." Not only was this *qì* the basis of all material substance, it also existed in a certain orderly arrangement and cyclical configuration. If this natural order of *qì* and *yīn yáng* were disturbed, calamities, including both illness and natural disasters such as earthquakes, would result.

Such an event is indeed recorded in the *Guó Yǔ* as having occurred in the San Chuan region in the second year of the reign of Zhou You Wang, an emperor during the end of the Western Zhou period (1066 B.C.E.–771 B.C.E.). The following explanation is attributed to Bo Yang Fu, a senior officer in the Kingdom of Zhou:

Thus the qì of heaven and earth cannot lose its natural order. If this order is disturbed, chaos will follow. The yáng subsides and cannot express and release. The yīn becomes forced and cannot sublimate. Thus, there was an earthquake. Today this earthquake occurred in San Chuan because the yáng lost its position and suppressed the yīn. The yáng lost its order but the result manifested in the yīn [i.e. the substance of the earth]. The source of the river will become obstructed. If the origin is obstructed, the country will be lost.

This explanation continues by extending the implication of comprehending the natural order of *qì*, *yīn*, and *yáng* to the conduct of government:

Because the understanding of the proper order of the qì of heaven and earth and yīn and yáng is the precondition of flourishing and prosperity, the monarch must follow the motions of qì in the conduct of his actions to protect himself and the whole country.

These general principles of the natural order implicit in the concept of *qì* were developed over the ensuing centuries.

The Four Seasons (*Sì Shí*). Title page of a Ming Dynasty version of Guǎn Zǐ (Annotated by Sikong Fang Xuan Ling of the Tang Dynasty).

In the work of Guan Zi, the statesman and philosopher of the Warring States period (475 B.C.E–221 B.C.E.), they achieved comprehensive and eloquent expression as a series of idealized relationships that correlated the four seasons with the conduct of social and political affairs. The following lengthy quotations are from Guan Zi's *The Four Seasons (Sì Shí)*:

Political orders must conform to the solar terms.[3] *Were it not for this orderly arrangement, time would flow on earth as it does in heaven, without limits or edges. Who would be able to comprehend anything?*

[3] The phrase "solar terms" refers to an elaborate ancient method of reckoning time according to the lunar calendar. This system comprised a comprehensive series of interrelationships that divided the 360 days of the lunar year into 24 solar terms. These solar terms correlated with "the ten heavenly stems" and "the twelve earthly branches."

Only the sage grasps the order of the four seasons. If there is no understanding of the four seasons, this will result in the loss of the entire country. There will be no understanding of how to grow the five grains. The country will fall into decline. Thus yīn and yáng is the greatest principle of heaven and earth. The four seasons form the greatest channel for yīn and yáng. All penalties and virtuous blessings mingle and issue from the four seasons. But what are the movements of Spring, Summer, Autumn, and Winter?

The east is named "xīng" 星*. Its solar term is called "Spring." Its qì is named "wind." The wind gives birth to wood and bones. Its virtuous blessings are joy and victory. Life issues forth in this season. Its proper social matters include issuing the commands to renovate and maintain the position of deities. Pray piously and sacrifice with money and other valuables. Worship the orthodox ancestor, yáng. Manage and build dams. Plough and weed. Plant trees and grain. Repair and maintain bridges and ferries. Dredge the irrigation canals. Build and repair houses and ensure that water channels are clear so they flow freely. Do away with hatred. Pardon punishments to connect the four directions. Then the gentle wind will follow and the sweet rain will fall. The people will enjoy longevity and the hundred insects will flourish and propagate.*

This is all known as the blessing of xīng. Xīng gives birth. It develops the wind. But if in Spring the order of Winter is employed, there will be withering and death. If the Autumnal order is followed, frost will come. If the order of Summer is pursued there will be exhaustion. Therefore, during the three months of Spring, the five political decrees shall be issued at the first, jiǎ 甲*, and second, yǐ* 乙*, of the ten heavenly stems.*[4]

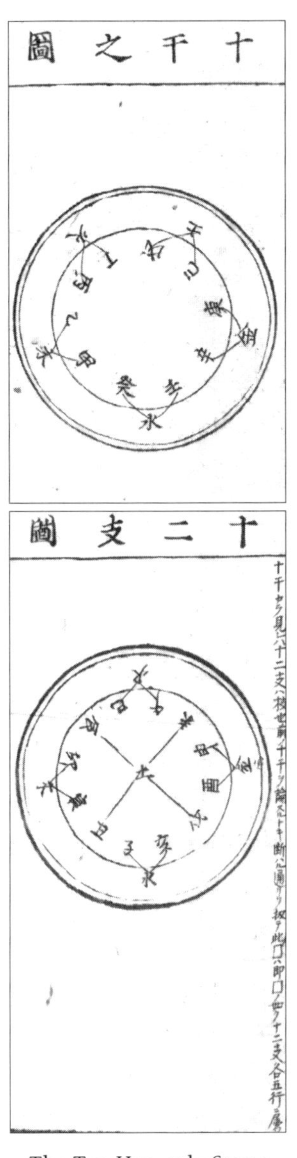

The Ten Heavenly Stems and the Twelve Earthly Branches, from the Song Dynasty text by Liu Weng Shu, *Sù Wèn Rù Shì Yùn Qì Lùn Ào.*

[4] The ten Heavenly Stems, like the twelve Earthly Branches, are parts of the ancient system of reckoning time and correlating changes of time with natural phenomena.

The first decree is to comfort young children and the lonely; pardon and release from punishments. The second decree is to grant official positions and award officials their salaries. The third decree is to break the ice and dredge the irrigation canals and renovate the tombs. The fourth decree is to flatten and smooth dangerous or difficult roads and rebuild and repair the borders of the fields; the divisions of the fields should also be clarified and repaired. The fifth decree is to forbid the killing of young animals and the breaking of any branches. If these five decrees are issued and implemented in due season, then the Spring rain will fall.

Here we see the correlation between the *qì* of nature and the conduct of people's lives. In time, such correlative thinking served as the foundation of a system of social, cultural, political, and economic rules and patterns of behavior that became the foundation of the next 2000 years of Chinese civilization. Rulers rose and fell. Invaders came and conquered. Yet this intrinsic Chinese way of life prevailed. From its very heart the pulse of the *qì* of heaven and earth beat steadily on.

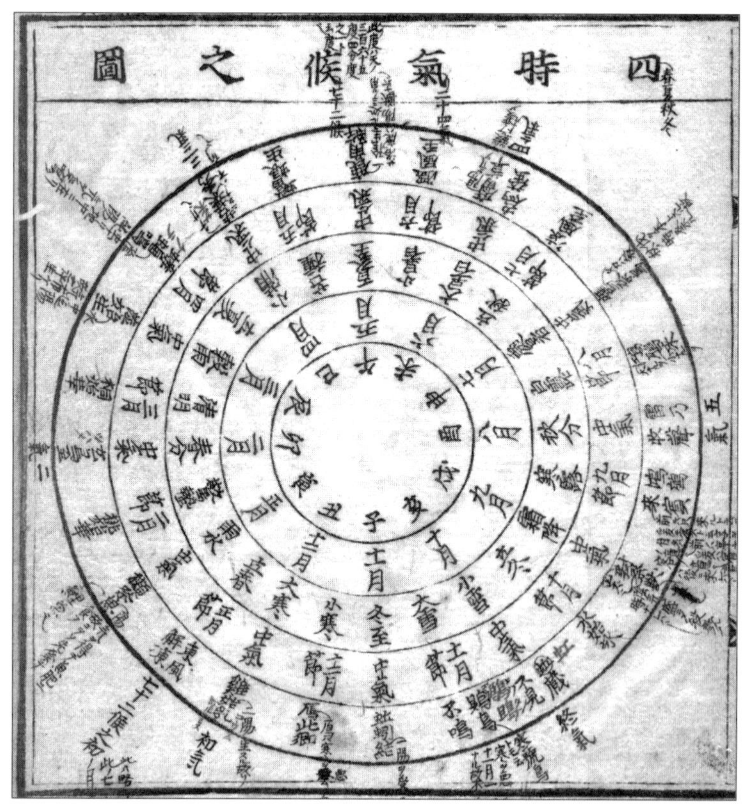

Diagram of Meterological Changes of the Four Seasons, from the Song Dynasty text by Liu Weng Shu, *Sù Wèn Rù Shì Yùn Qì Lùn Ào*.

To give a complete sense of this ancient blueprint of Chinese life and civilization, here is the balance of Guan Zi's treatise on the four seasons:

The southerly direction is named for the Sun, rì 日. *Its solar term is called "Summer." Its qì is named "yáng"* 陽. *Yáng gives birth to fire and to qì. Its virtuous blessing rewards officials, pardons punishments, and composes court music [based upon the ancient melodies]. Its social matters are to order the appraisal and awards of official positions and salaries; to go out and inspect the countryside; to build shrines with care; and to reward persons of virtue.*

襍故巧佞而好利燕之水萃下而弱沈滯而襍故其民愚戇而
好貞輕疾而易死沈故愚戇而好貞萃襍故輕疾而易死也宋之水輕勁而
清故其民閒易而好正輕故易清勁故好正也是以聖人之化世
也其解在水言解人之邪正嘗水而知故水一則人心正一謂不襍水清
則民心易一則欲不污人心既一故欲不污穢民心易則行無邪
易直則無邪也是以聖人之治於世也不人告也不戶說也其
樞在水樞主運轉者也言欲轉化於人但順水之理故曰其樞在水也
四時第四十

管子卷十四　五　短語十四

管子曰令有時王者命令必有其時無時則必視順天之所以來
視謂觀而察之若不得時則必觀察其所致改革以順天道之來也五漫漫六惛惛孰知
之哉漫漫曠遠貌惛惛微暗貌五謂每時之政其理曠遠六謂陰陽四時其理微暗既漫且惛故知之者
少也唯聖人知四時不知四時乃失國之基不知五穀之
故國家乃路路謂失其常居故天曰信明地曰信聖言能信順天地之道
則而行之者日明日聖也四時曰正順行四時之令日正也其王信明聖其臣
乃正君明聖則能用賢材故正也何以知其王之信明信聖也曰慎
使能而善聽信之謂能聽信賢材之人使能之謂明使任賢能則為明也聽
信之謂聖既聽其言又信其事所以為聖信明聖者皆受天賞信明者天福也

Guǎn Zǐ, Chapter 14, Page 5, "The Four Seasons."

These all aid the raising of the yáng qì. Then the Great Heat of Summer will arrive and the season's rains will fall. The five grains and the one hundred different fruits will produce a bountiful harvest. These are known as the blessings of the Sun.

The center is named Earth, tǔ 土. *The order of Earth is to assist with the entrances and exits of the four seasons to adjust and control the wind and rain. The Earth nourishes and increases the strength for reproduction. It generates the skin and muscles. Its virtuous blessings include peace and harmony, balance and equanimity. It holds the central, upright position. It selflessly supplements the four seasons: the breeding of Spring; the growth of Summer; the harvest of Autumn; the storage of Winter. Therefore the Great Cold arrives and the country flourishes and prospers. The four directions are established in their proper order. This is known as the virtuous blessing of suì 歲.*[5]

Suì rules over harmony, and harmony brings the rain. But if Summer follows the order of Spring there will be harmful winds. If it follows the order of Autumn, harmful waters come. If the order of Winter is followed in Summer there will be withering and falling [of growing things]. Therefore, in the three months of Summer the five political decrees are released at the third, bǐng 丙, and fourth, dīng 丁, of the ten heavenly stems.

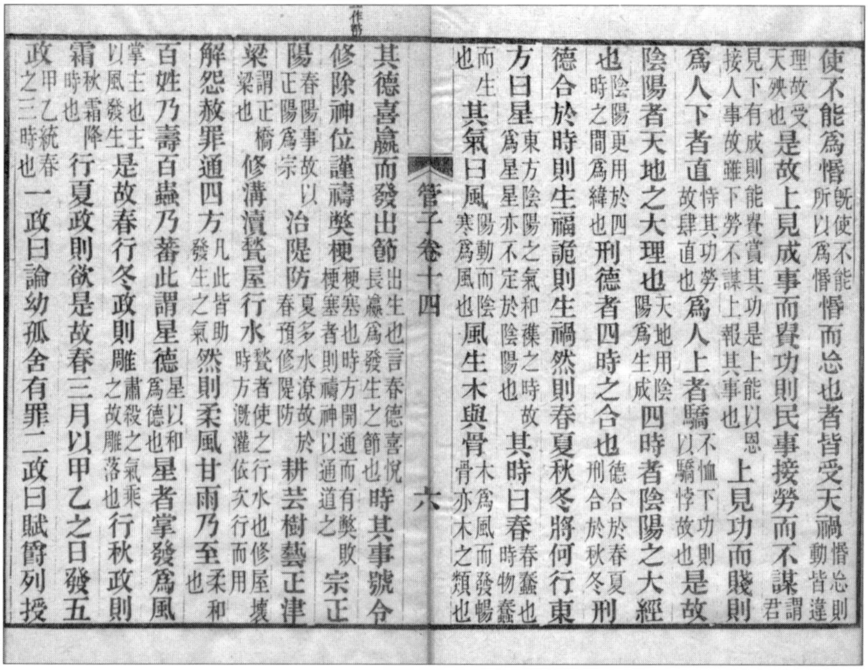
使不能為惛既使不能所以為惛惛而忿也者皆受天禍惛忿則動皆違
理故受天殃也是故上見成事而貴功則民事接勞而不謀謂君
見下有成則能賚賞其功是上能以恩接人事故雖下勞不謀上報其事也上見功而賤則
為人下者直恃其功勞故肆直也為人上者驕不恤下功則以驕悖故也是故
陰陽者天地之大理也天地用陰陽為生成四時者陰陽之大經
也陰陽更用於四時之間為緯也刑德者四時之合也德合於春夏刑合於秋冬刑
德合於時則生福詭則生禍然則春夏秋冬將何行東
方曰星東方陰陽之氣和蘖之時故為星星亦不定於陰陽也其時曰春春蠢也時物蠢
而生也其氣曰風陽動而陰寒為風也風生木與骨木為風而發暢骨亦木之類也
管子卷十四　六
其德喜嬴而發出節出生也言春德喜悅長嬴為發生之節也時其事號令
修除神位謹禱弊梗梗寒也時方開通而有弊敗梗塞者則禱神以通道之宗正
陽春陽事故以正陽為宗治隄防夏多水潦故於春預修隄防耕芸樹藝正津
梁謂正橋梁也修溝瀆甃屋行水甃者使之行水也修屋壞時方溉灌依穴行而用
解怨赦罪通四方凡此皆助發生之氣然則柔風甘雨乃至柔和也
百姓乃壽百蟲乃蕃此謂星德星以和為德也星者掌發為風
掌主也主以風發生是故春行冬政則雕肅殺之氣乘之故雕落也行秋政則
霜秋霜降時也行夏政則欲是故春三月以甲乙之日發五
政甲乙統春之三時也一政曰論幼孤舍有罪二政曰賦爵列授

Guǎn Zǐ, Chapter 14, Page 6, "The Four Seasons."

The first decree is to seek out those who have made contributions and given outstanding service and raise their position. The second decree is to develop the sealed land and excavate old houses to unearth the cellars for storing goods. The third decree is to issue orders forbidding doors to remain open or locks to be left unlocked. Forbid neglecting to wear official headgear. Ensure that drainage ditches are clear and

[5] The Chinese term *suì* 歲 like *xīng* 星 for Spring and *rì* 日 for Summer, is assigned to the Earth as its heavenly coordinate. It is the name of the planet we know in English as Jupiter. It is also a term for the precession of the equinoxes.

drain the fields. The fourth decree is to seek people of virtue who have bestowed kindness on others and reward them generously. The fifth decree is to issue orders that forbid that traps be set to hunt wild beasts; forbid the killing of birds. If these five decrees are implemented in coordination with the season, the Summer rains will fall.

The westerly direction is named chén 辰 *[one of the twenty-eight constellations; see the illustration on page 38]. Its solar term is Autumn. Its qì is named yīn* 陰*. Yīn gives birth to metal and armor. Its virtuous blessings are sorrow and grief, tranquility and forthrightness, strictness and obedience. Its social matters are the issuance of orders to prohibit people from engaging in excessive violence and to advise the people to gather together. People should evaluate their possessions to accumulate savings. Take stock of the capable officials and assemble the talented. Let wealth be stored. Do not let the people slow down. Rid that which is not favored. Satisfy desires. Trust and justice must be established. These are the blessings of chén* 辰*. It controls gathering. Gathering together is the nature of yīn. If in Autumn one follows the order of Spring, there will yet be flourishing. If the order of Summer is implemented water will come. If Winter's orders are followed, there will be exhaustion.*

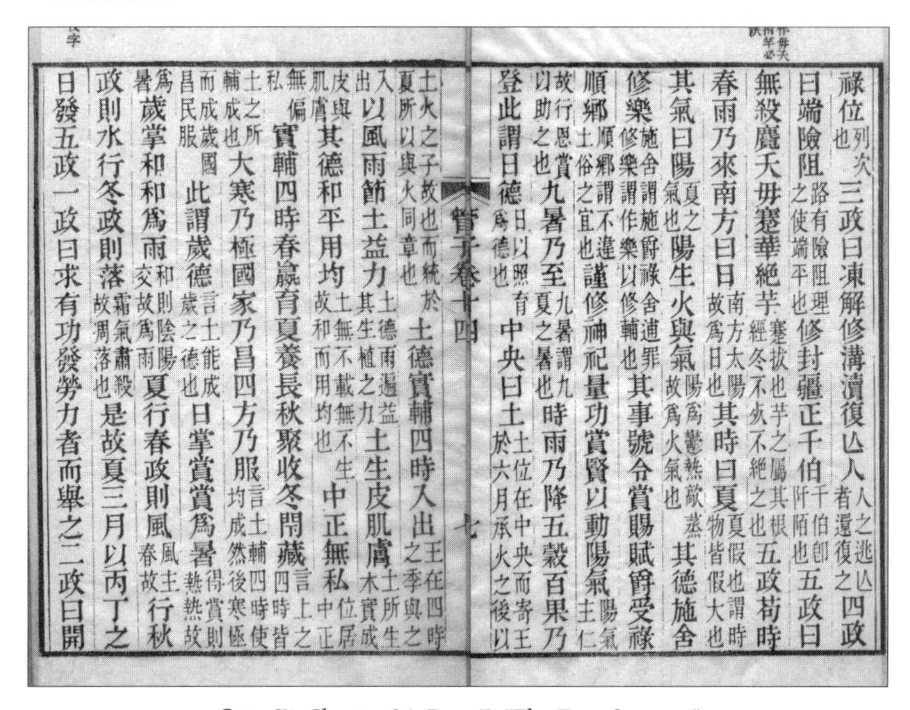
祿位列次也三政曰凍解修溝瀆復亾人人之逃亾者還復之四政
曰端險阻路有險阻理之使端平也修封疆正千伯千伯郎阡陌也五政曰
無殺麛夭毋蹇華絕芋蹇拔也芋之屬其根經冬不死不絕之也五政苟時
春雨乃來南方曰日南方太陽故為日也其時曰夏夏假也謂時物皆假大也
其氣曰陽夏之氣也陽生火與氣陽為鬱熱歊蒸故為火氣也其德施舍
修樂施舍謂施爵祿舍逋罪修樂謂作樂以修輔也其事號令賞賜賦爵受祿
順鄉順鄉謂不違土俗之宜也謹修神祀量功賞賢以動陽氣陽氣主仁
故行恩賞以助之也九暑乃至九暑謂九夏之暑也時雨乃降五穀百果乃
登此謂日德日以照育為德也中央曰土土位在中央而寄王於六月承火之後以
管子卷十四　七
土火之子故也而統於夏所以與火同章也土德實輔四時入出王在四時之季與之
入出以風雨節土益力土德雨遍益其生植之力土生皮肌膚土所生木實成
皮與肌膚其德和平用均土無不載無不生故和而用均也中正無私位居中正
無私偏實輔四時春嬴育夏養長秋聚收冬閉藏言上之四時皆
土之所輔成也大寒乃極國家乃昌四方乃服言土輔四時使均成然後寒極
而成歲國昌民服此謂歲德言土能成歲之德也日掌賞賞為暑得賞則熱熱故
為暑歲掌和和為雨和則陰陽交故為雨夏行春政則風風主春故行秋
政則水行冬政則落霜氣肅殺故凋落也是故夏三月以丙丁之
日發五政一政曰求有功發勞力者而舉之二政曰開

Guǎn Zǐ, Chapter 14, Page 7, "The Four Seasons."

During the term of Autumn's three months, issue the five political decrees at the seventh, gēng 庚, and eighth, xīn 辛, of the heavenly stems. The first decree is to forbid gambling and avoid quarrels. Resolve jealousy and disputes. The second decree is to prohibit the display of sword blades and the knives of the five armies [i.e. refrain from warfare]. The third decree is to warn traveling farmers to hasten home and gather together. The fourth decree is to repair breaches and fill in gaps. The fifth decree is to build and repair walls and to strengthen doors and gates. If these five decrees are implemented in coordination with the season, the five grains can be abundantly gathered.

久墳久墳瘞之處開通之也發故屋辟故窌以假貸辟開也三政曰
令禁扇去笠禁扇去笠者不欲令人褻盛陽之氣毋扱免禁扱祍免者亦不欲人惡盛
陽之氣也除急漏田廬田中之廬欲漏之不欲人惡盛陽之氣也四政曰求有德
賜布施於民者而賞之五政曰令禁罝設禽獸謂設罝以取禽
獸也毋殺飛鳥五政苟時夏雨乃至也西方曰辰辰星日交會也
秋陰陽適中故爲辰其時曰秋秋揫也時物成熟揫歛之其氣曰陰秋之氣也陰生
金與甲陰氣凝結堅實故生金爲爪甲也其德憂哀靜正嚴順秋氣悽惻故以
憂恤哀憐爲德靜正陰之性也嚴順謂德雖嚴然順時而爲之也居不敢淫佚順秋氣而靜居
不敢爲淫逸過失也其事號令毋使民淫暴順旅聚收謂順時理軍旅聚而
管子卷十四 八
收之也量民資以畜聚賞彼羣幹衆有武幹人當賞之聚彼羣材材謂
可以充兵器之材當收聚之百物乃收使民毋怠時云收歛出師聚裝人無懈怠故
所惡其察所欲必得察所惡之方而伐之則得其所欲也我信則克我既誠信
故能克敵此謂辰德辰以收歛殺姦邪爲德也辰掌收收爲陰收聚冬閉藏故爲陰
秋行春政則榮春發榮也行夏政則水夏多行水潦也行冬政則耗
冬肅殺損耗也是故秋三月以庚辛之日發五政一政曰禁博
塞博塞長姦邪故禁之圉小辯鬭譯跽小辯則利口覆國及譯傳言語相疾忌爲鬭訟者皆
當禁圉之也二政曰毋見五兵之刃時或出師掩襲故藏五兵之刃也三政
曰慎旅農趣聚收四政曰補鉠塞坼師旅營農當慎收之秋方閉藏故令

Guǎn Zǐ, Chapter 14, Page 8, "The Four Seasons."

The northern direction is named for the Moon, yuè 月. Its solar term is Winter. Its qì is named "cold." The cold gives birth to water and blood. Its virtuous blessings are purity and honesty, gentility and forgiveness, care and thoroughness. Its social matters are to issue orders prohibiting travel so that the people do not move about the country. Order them to remain in their places, then the Earth qì will not drain away. Judge cases and execute punishments. Do not pardon crimes so as to coordinate with the yīn qì. Then the Great Cold arrives; the army grows strong, the five grains ripen, and the country is prosperous and in all four directions there will be obedience.

This is known as the virtuous blessing of the Moon. The Moon rules over punishments. Punishment is cold. But if Winter implements the orders of Spring, the qì will leak. If Summer's orders are followed, there will be thunder. If Autumn's orders are implemented, there will be drought. Therefore, during the three months of Winter, issue the five decrees at the dates of the ninth, rén 壬, *and tenth, guǐ* 癸, *of the ten heavenly stems. The first decree is to engage in discussion with the people of their situations and circumstances and to provide pensions for the elderly. The second decree is to follow the yīn qì; repair and rebuild the shrines; offer official positions; reward the officials their salaries; award and arrange official offices. The third decree is to check and correct financial records; do not excavate stores of natural resources. The fourth decree is to apprehend the crafty and the evil; reward people who capture thieves. The fifth decree is to prohibit moving; tightly control traveling and do not let the people wander about; resist the separation of families and marriages.*

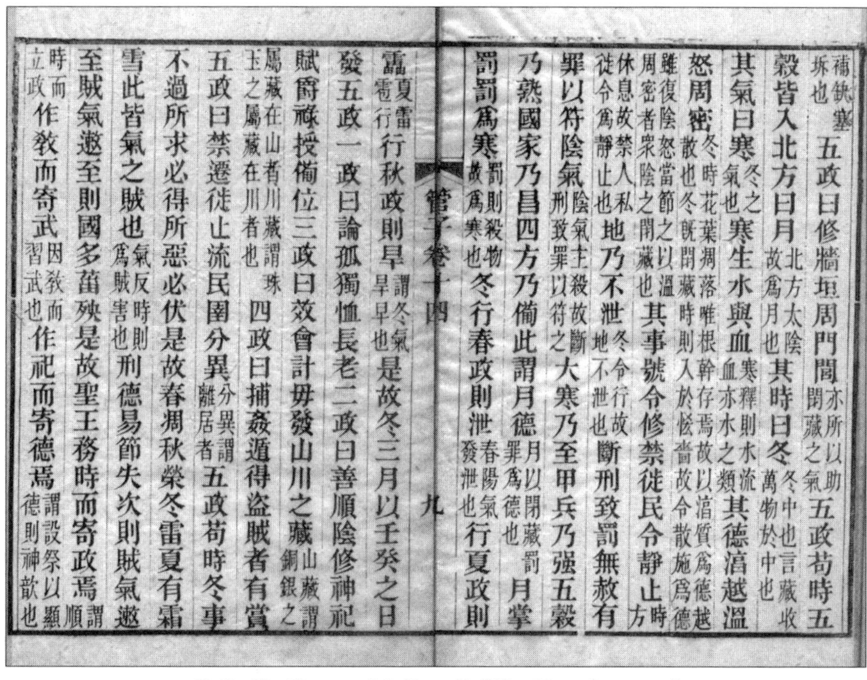
補缺塞坼也五政曰修牆垣周門閭亦所以助閉藏之氣五政苟時五
穀皆入北方曰月北方太陰故爲月也其時曰冬冬中也言藏收萬物於中也
其氣曰寒冬之氣也寒生水與血寒釋則水流血亦水之類其德湻越溫
怒周密冬時花葉凋落唯根幹存焉故以湻質爲德越散也冬既閉藏時則入於惓嗇故令散施爲德
雖復陰怒當節之以溫周密者衆陰之閉藏也其事號令修禁徙民令靜止時方
休息故禁人私徙令爲靜止也地乃不泄冬令行故地不泄也斷刑致罰無赦有
罪以符陰氣陰氣主殺故斷刑致罪以符之大寒乃至甲兵乃強五穀
乃熟國家乃昌四方乃備此謂月德月以閉藏罰罪爲德也月掌
罰罰爲寒罰則殺物故爲寒也冬行春政則泄春陽氣發泄也行夏政則

管子卷十四　九

雷夏雷雹行行秋政則旱謂冬氣旱早也是故冬三月以壬癸之日
發五政一政曰論孤獨恤長老二政曰善順陰修神祀
賦爵祿授備位三政曰效會計毋發山川之藏山藏謂銅銀之
屬藏在山者川藏謂珠玉之屬藏在川者也四政曰捕姦遁得盜賊者有賞
五政曰禁遷徙止流民圉分異分異謂離居者五政苟時冬事
不過所求必得所惡必伏是故春凋秋榮冬雷夏有霜
雪此皆氣之賊也氣反時則爲賊害也刑德易節失次則賊氣遬
至賊氣遬至則國多菑殃是故聖王務時而寄政焉謂順
時而立政作教而寄武因教而習武也作祀而寄德焉謂設祭以顯德則神歆也

Guǎn Zǐ, Chapter 14, Page 9, "The Four Seasons."

If these five decrees are coordinated with the season, there will be no falsity in these Winter matters. Hence desires will be fulfilled and evil will be extinguished. Thus the withering in Spring, the flourishing in Autumn, the thunder in Winter, the frost and snow in Summer: these all belong to the evils of qì. If penalties and virtuous blessings exchange their positions and escape control, the evil qì will not be slow in coming. Once evil qì arrives, the country will be thrown into turmoil and disaster. Thus the sage king seizes the right moment to act and endows his policies accordingly. He implements these teachings and fortifies his armies. He offers sacrifices to the gods and ancestors and is thus endowed with virtuous blessings. In these ways, the sage king coordinates his actions with the movements of heaven and earth.

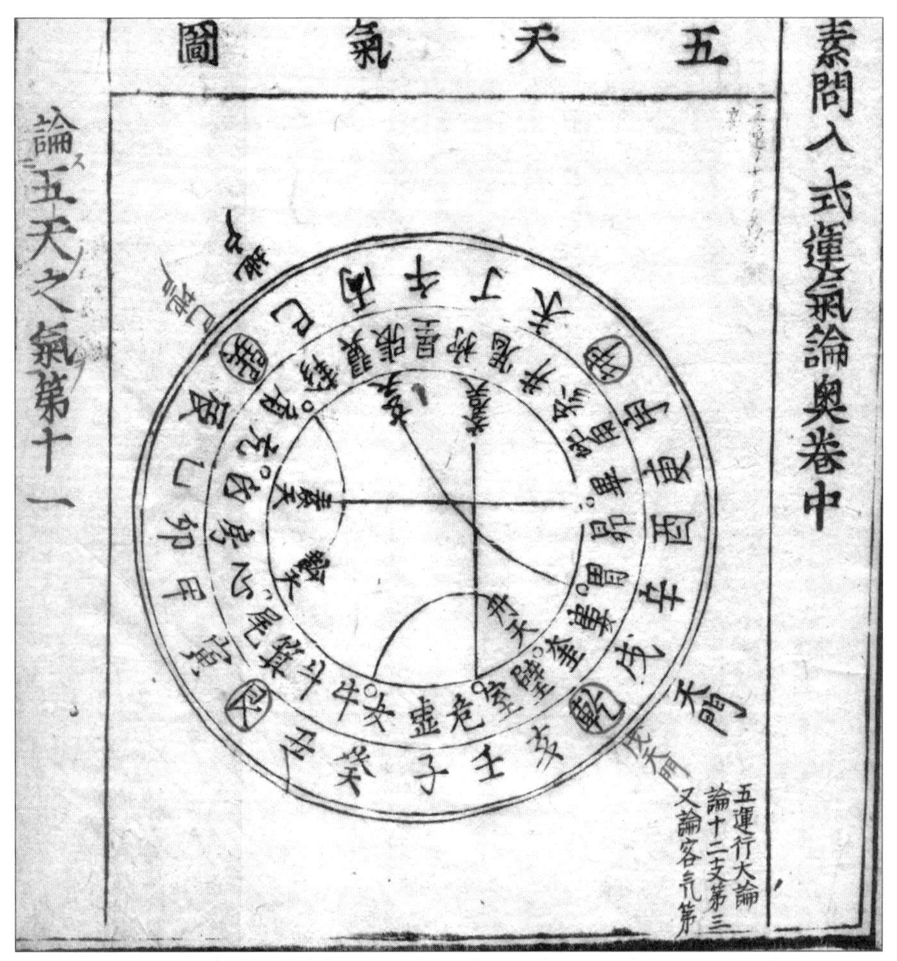

Wǔ Tiān Qì Tú, diagram of the Five Heavenly Qì, showing the Twenty-eight constellations with the Ten Heavenly Stems and Twelve Earthly Branches, from the Song Dynasty text by Liu Weng Shu, *Sù Wèn Rù Shì Yùn Qì Lùn Ào.*

The sun controls yáng. The moon controls yīn. Jupiter controls harmony. Yáng symbolizes the virtuous blessings. Yīn symbolizes punishments. Harmony symbolizes social matters. Therefore, when a solar eclipse appears the country has mismanaged the virtuous blessings. When a lunar eclipse appears punishments have been mismanaged. If a comet appears, the country has strayed from peace and harmony. If winds come and vie with the sun obscuring brightness, the country has mismanaged political affairs. [These are all unwelcome signs foreboding ill.] Thus the sage king cultivates his virtue when a solar eclipse occurs. He adjusts punishments when there is a lunar eclipse. He balances things and strives for peace and harmony when comets appear. When the wind contends with the sun for brightness, he sees to the proper management of political affairs. These four reasons allow the sage king exemption from the punishments of heaven and earth, when they are followed with sincerity. Then the five grains can be harvested aplenty. The six domesticated animals will breed, and the strength of the army will increase.

此三者聖王所以合於天地之行也天地之行唯此三者而已日掌
陽月掌陰星掌和陽爲德陰爲刑和爲事是故日食則
失德之國惡之月食則失刑之國惡之彗星見則失和
之國惡之失則當受罰故其所失各以其所類而與惡也風與日爭明則失生
之國惡之日惡風且熱旱災咸矣方生之物皆枯悴矣此失生德也故失生之國惡也是故
聖王日食則修德月食則修刑彗星見則修和風與日
爭明則修生此四者聖王所以免於天地之誅也信能
行之五穀蕃息六畜殖而甲兵強治積則昌暴虐積則
亾道生天地道者自然能生天地也德出賢人德者賢人所修爲故能生賢也道

管子卷十四　十

生德法道則成德也德生正德修則理自正正生事正直則事幹是以聖王
治天下窮則反終則始德始於春長於夏刑始於秋流
於冬謂刑於冬而休息也刑德不失四時如一皆順時而成故如一刑德離
鄉時乃逆行鄉方也作事不成必有大殃月有三政月三旬政
異故曰三政也王事必理以爲久長王者行事必順三政之理然後可以長久不中
者死失理者亡中猶合也不合三政者則死違失其理必敗亡國有四時固執
王事固執四時之政以輔行王事四守有所謂守四時令得其所三政執輔執月
之三政輔行己德也
五行第四十一

Guǎn Zǐ, Chapter 14, Page 10, "The Four Seasons."

If these factors are coordinated and managed wisely, the country will flourish. But if they are implemented with violence and tyranny, the country will be subjugated. Dào gives birth to heaven and earth. Virtue gives birth to persons of virtue. Dào gives birth to virtue. Virtue gives birth to righteousness. Righteousness gives birth to civility. Thus, the sage king manages the whole world wisely based upon such matters. After exhaustion, there is rebirth. Every end is followed by a new beginning. Virtue begins in Spring. It grows during the Summer. Punishments begin in Autumn to be enforced in Winter. If virtue and punishments do not falter from their harmonious ways, the four seasons will remain in harmony. But if punishments and harmony do not accord with established order, the four seasons will be reversed. Failure in the management of social matters will lead to catastrophe.

There are three political divisions of every month which the king must govern wisely in order to prolong the country's life. If such government is not properly conducted, death is the result. If this governing is not conducted according to logic, the whole country will be subjugated. The country has four seasons. The dominant factor of politics is to follow them strictly. Only then can the four seasons protect their respective limits. Then implementation of monthly politics assists in securing the blessings of heaven and earth.

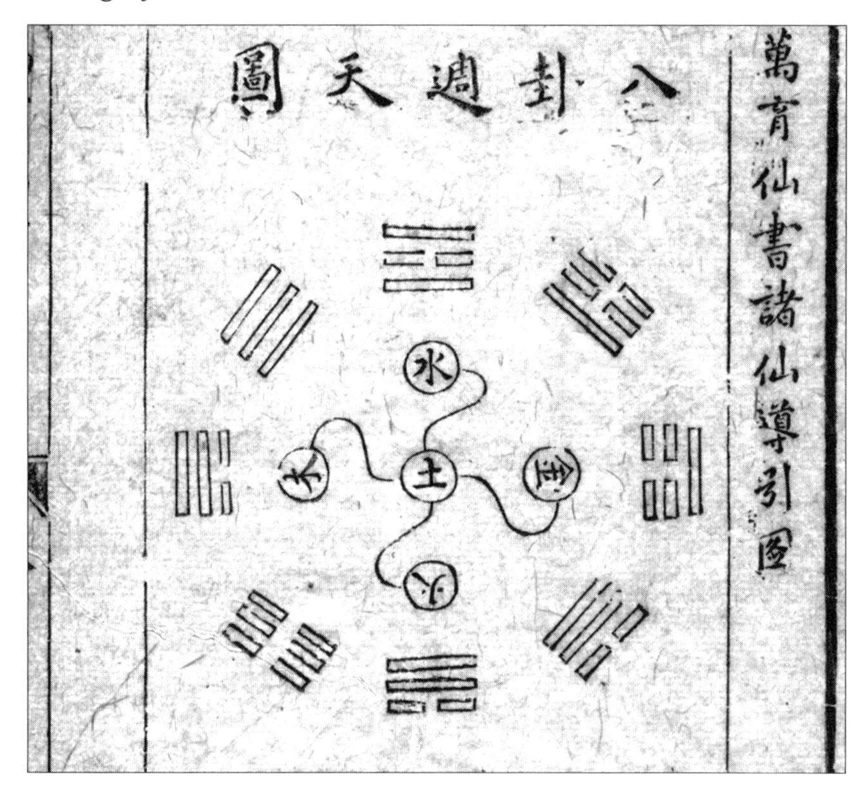

Bā Guà Zhōu Tiān Tú, illustration from the Ming Dynasty text by Cao Wu Ji, *Wàn Yù Xiān Shū*. It shows the natural cycling of the five phases in correspondence with the eight trigrams.

Such material can be considered as a blueprint of the social contract in ancient Chinese civilization. Although the letter of these admonitions is no longer observed by way of official policy, the spirit of harmonizing with the cyclical movements of nature still animates much of cultural life in modern China. Moreover, many customary observances, such as the Chinese New Year or Spring Festival celebrations, can be traced directly to this notion of the Grand Order of the *qì* of humankind in accordance with the *qì* of nature. This fundamental concern with establishing harmony between humans and nature appears in the oldest traditions native to China. Thus, when we dig even deeper into the cultural soil that holds the roots of ancient China, we discover the rich source of Daoist philosophy, the ultimate expression of natural law. In this ancient earth rests the germ of *qì*.

SECTION THREE: *QÌ* AND *DÀO*

Xīu Qì Tú (Resting and Leisure), from the Ming Dynasty Text, *Chéng Shì Mò Yuán*.

Lao Zi was not the organizer of the Daoist religion, but his is certainly the name most commonly identified with the origins of Daoist philosophy. The biography of this archetypal "Old Man" of the Spring and Autumn period

(770 B.C.E.–476 B.C.E.) is found in Si Ma Qian's *Book of History (Shǐ Jì).* Regardless of its historicity, the story of Lao Zi's life has gained currency in China and throughout the world and serves as the standard explanation for the origin of one of the most read and translated of the ancient Daoist classics, the *Dào Dé Jīng.* It is a cornerstone of both the Daoist philosophy and religion.

Lao Zi, from the Ming Dynasty text *Liè Xiān Quán Zhuàn.*

Briefly, the story goes that there lived in the state of Lu a man named Li Er or Lao Dan who worked as a civil servant, custodian of the official library. After serving his appointed term, he grew tired of the ways of the world and decided to withdraw from civilization to live out his days as a hermit. As he was about to pass through the gate that marked the boundary between the state of Lu and the wilderness beyond, the keeper of the gate asked him to record his thoughts so that they might be studied by future generations. Complying with this request, the old man sat down and wrote out 5000 characters to express his understanding of the world. Arranged into eighty-one chapters, the *Dào Dé Jīng* is the only trace Lao Zi left behind. In some versions of the legend, he lived well beyond 200 years in the world of nature beyond the gate, the result of harmonizing with the *dào* of nature.

The *dào* of Lao Zi is hard to grasp. Indeed, the *Dào Dé Jīng* begins with words that stand as an admonition to those who seek to study and follow this mystical path. "The *dào* that can be expressed [as *dào*] is not the eternal *dào*. The name that can be named is not its eternal name." In Chapter 25, there is an elaboration upon the paradoxical difficulties associated with the *dào*.

> *There is a chaotic thing, born before heaven and earth. So silent. So empty. Unique and unchanging. Circling endlessly, it could be called the Mother of All Things Under Heaven. I do not know its name. I reluctantly call it dào, and if forced to do so, would describe it as great.*

Over and over such words appear throughout this ancient text to describe the *dào*, its nature and characteristics. The *dào* is "elusive and evanescent." It is "empty, yet use will never drain it." *Dào* is "vacant, dark, yet contains a vital essence." This essence is "very real and can be verified."

Si Ma Cheng Zhen, a Daoist immortal. From the Ming Dynasty text *Liè Xiān Quán Zhuàn.*

Clearly what the *Dào Dé Jīng* describes as *dào* is the origin and basis of all creation. Recall the quotation cited earlier, from Chapter 42 of the *Dào Dé Jīng*:

> *Dào gives birth to One.*
> *One gives birth to Two.*
> *Two gives birth to Three.*
> *Three gives birth to the Ten Thousand Things.*

Yet in Chapter 39, there are words which seem to contradict or at least confound the meaning of this passage.

> *In times past Oneness appeared in the following pattern: The heavens attained Oneness and became clear; The earth attained Oneness and settled; The spirits attained Oneness and became numinous; Valleys attained Oneness and became reproductive; All things attained Oneness and became alive; Kings and officials attained Oneness and became the orthodoxy of the world.*[6]

Some light is shed on such perplexing issues in a work entitled *Lu's Annals of Spring and Autumn (Lǔ Shì Chūn Qīu):*

> *Thus dào is sublime essence. It cannot be formalized. It cannot be named. Yet to name it, reluctantly, it is the Great Oneness (tài yī).*

The Great Oneness (tài yī)

However, wrestling with explanations of the *dào* can be like struggling to get free from quicksand. For those who nonetheless desire to penetrate the quagmire more deeply, the relationship between *qì* and *dào* can serve as a lifeline. Centuries after the *Dào Dé Jīng* was written, Daoist masters of the Ming Dynasty compiled their insights in another Daoist classic, *The Instrument for Determining the Purpose of*

[6] from Lao-Tzu: "My words are very easy to understand," *Lectures on the Tao Te Ching* by Cheng Man-Ching. Translated from the Chinese by Tam C. Gibbs. North Atlantic Books, 1981.

Life (Xìng Mìng Guī Zhǐ). In one section of this book, the "Explanation of the Great *Dào*," we read the following passage:

> *The dào positioned heaven and earth. It nourishes everything in the world. It reveals the sun and moon, gives birth to the five phases. Its manifestations are as numerous as the grains of sand in the Heng River. Yet it is still the dào even if it were to produce but a single grain without companion.*
> *It is called the dào if in a state of chaos, and things return to endless confusion.*
> *It is called the dào when the pivot of creation gathers to release all souls from limbo.*
> *It is called the dào when understanding enters the mind with no manifestation of any kind.*
> *It is called the dào when there is no way to turn away from the confrontation of life and death.*
> *It is called the dào when the situation is oppressed yet [one] still can hold respect and honor.*
> *It is called the dào when living among the gloom everything is dim yet [one] still holds brightness high.*
> *It is called the dào when it is small as dust.*
> *It is called the dào when it contains the entire universe.*
> *It is called the dào when it cannot be penetrated from any direction.*
> *It is called the dào when it manifests as Buddhas and Gods.*
> *You could discourse upon it for more than 5000 volumes, use 5000 words to describe it.*
> *Thus [we call it] the dào, but what is it?*
> *To use but one word to explain it: it is qì.*

The passage continues with a vivid depiction of events which, again, bear a metaphoric resemblance to the conditions described by contemporary cosmologists in the Big Bang and the first moments following the creation of the universe.

> *Thus originally there was one qì, a gathering mist. There was chaos stretching to infinity, constantly changing, an enshrouding mist containing motion. It holds all intelligence, all sublime marvels. It's called the Great Unity, tài yǐ* 太乙*, which has the same meaning as tài yī* 太一*. It is the beginning of non-being. Thus it begins: the dào. And thus it is called that which has no beginning.*

Thus, the birth of heaven and earth begins with the motion of one turbulent qì. The emptiness begins to open and shudder. The yīn and yáng interact impelling the confluence of black and white, the confluence and congealing of something and nothingness, shooting across the void to penetrate one another, mixing the chaos, the pulsing emptiness.

Thus the man of virtue sublimates. Herein are contained the marvels and mysterious changes of shén míng [enlightenment]. Thus are the limits [of the cosmos] established elusively and evanescently. This is known as the Great Change, tài yì 太易. *This is the beginning of that which has a beginning. It is known by the phrase, "Dào gives birth to One."*

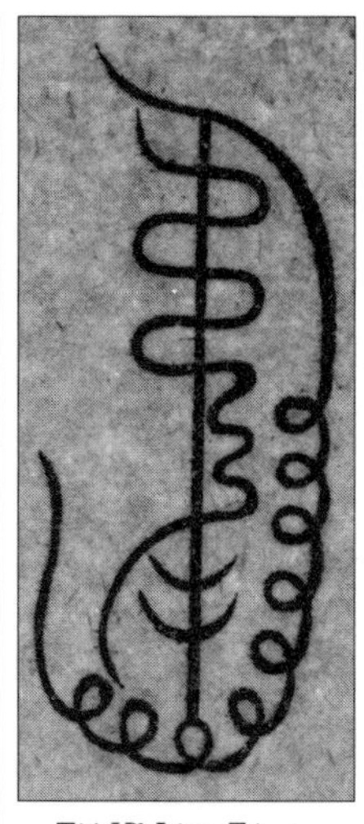

Tài Yī Líng Fú, a Daoist talisman.

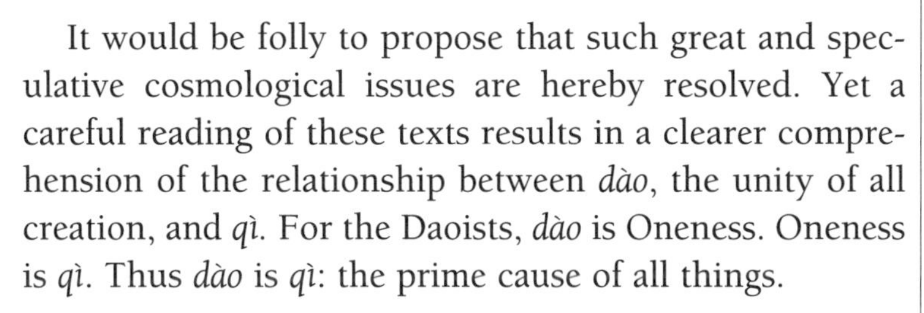

It would be folly to propose that such great and speculative cosmological issues are hereby resolved. Yet a careful reading of these texts results in a clearer comprehension of the relationship between *dào*, the unity of all creation, and *qì*. For the Daoists, *dào* is Oneness. Oneness is *qì*. Thus *dào* is *qì*: the prime cause of all things.

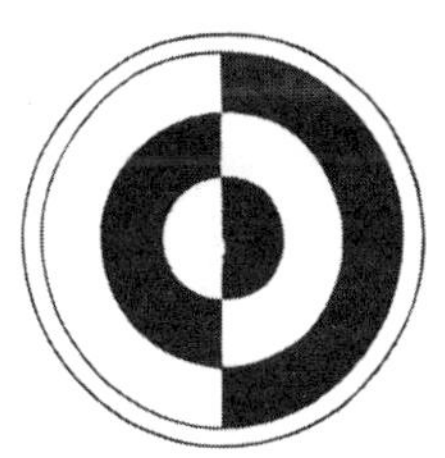

Tài Jí Tú, a version of the *tài jí* diagram.

Yet there is something less than equivalence between *dào* and *qì*. The status of "that which comes before the beginning" is reserved for the mysterious concept, *dào*, as noted in this passage from Chapter 4 of the *Dào Dé Jīng*:

The dào is empty, yet when used can not be filled.
So deep it is, Ah!
It seems to be the ancestor of all things.

In the Daoist conceptual hierarchy, then, *dào* is primary, rather more fundamental than *qì*. The role of *qì* in this hierarchy of essential causes and influences is that of an intermediary agent between the *dào* and all creation. Like the *dào*, *qì* is formless, yet it exists in the essential substances of everything in existence. Man's creation and continued existence depends upon it. This is made clear in the following series of questions from Chapter 10 of the *Dào Dé Jīng*.

專氣致柔能嬰兒乎

zhuān qì zhì róu néng yīng ér hū

Can one unify the spirit of the blood
And the spirit of the breath and
Keep them from separating?
In concentrating the qì to attain resiliency
Can one be like a baby?

In his "Lectures on Lao Zi," from which the above quotations are taken,[7] Cheng Man Ching comments on these lines as follows:

> *Concentrating the qì refers to breathing. . . . Regarding "to attain resiliency," Qi Bo [the physician and interlocutor of the Yellow Emperor in the Yellow Emperor's Classic of Internal Medicine] said, "Let the circulatory systems of blood and qì flow freely." This is the basis of Lao Zi's emphasis on the cultivation of qì, as in the lines, "the tendons are resilient and the grip is firm" and "reverse old age and become like a child."*

Such concepts echo throughout the work of other Daoist writers. Another principal exponent of what came to be known as the Lao Zhuang School of Thought was the Daoist sage, Zhuang Zi. Like Lao Zi, he affirmed the *dào* as the noumenon of the universe, the highest law and eternal principle, the ultimate truth. Zhuang Zi, however, emphasized understanding the *dào* in human terms. In so doing he provides further evidence for the relationship between *qì* and *dào* and correlates this relationship to the human condition.

In a work called *Zhi Travels North (Zhī Běi Yóu)* Zhuang Zi says:

> *The life of humankind is the gathering of qì. This gathering creates life. If it disperses, death results. If life and death belong to the same category, then what is there for me to worry about? Thus the ten thousand things are just one Unity. Thus the saying that in all the universe there is but one qì. The sage treasures Oneness.*

---

[7] *Op. cit.*

In Chapter Four, we will explore the implications of such concepts in the development of medicine in China. Among the most basic of the defining characteristics of traditional Chinese medicine is the precept that the human body is a microcosm of the entire universe. Such notions clearly spring from these Daoist sources. The *qì* of Lao Zi and Zhuang Zi flows throughout the body of traditional Chinese medical theory. Until today, the hands of well-trained practitioners are guided by this ancient *qì*.

Lu Dao Zhang, from the Ming Dynasty text *Liè Xiān Quán Zhuàn.*

Thus when Zhuang Zi says, "If the *qì* of *yīn* and *yáng* are not in harmony there will be disaster," doctors of Chinese medicine listen closely and learn well. When he adds, "to protect the body and its essence from exhaustion is called being able to change with the changes of nature," theorists and clinicians alike pay heed.

From the foregoing we can see that the concept of *qì* was developed and refined by ancient Daoists into expressions that have proven extraordinarily useful for thousands of years. But the *qì* of ancient China is too vast and all-encompassing to be contained in but one philosophical school. Not only the Daoists discoursed on the nature of *qì* and its relationship to nature and human affairs. The phenomena of *qì* plays a central, albeit more subtle role in the humanism, order, and respect for the individuals and institutions of the past that characterize the school of thought that evolved in the name of China's most famous sage, Kong Zi, Confucius.[8]

Section Four: The *Qì* of Kong Zi, Meng Zi, and the Confucian School

The Confucian school of thought has exerted unparalleled influence over Chinese civilization. Among the chief components of Confucian philosophy, the concept of "benevolence and humanism" or *rén* 仁 is perhaps the

[8] The commonly known name of the Chinese philosopher Kong Zi is Confucius. We use "Confucius" throughout for the sake of simplicity.

most prominent. Of the modern exponents of the Confucian school of thought who brought their philosophy to the Western world, few equal and fewer still exceed the late Cheng Man Ching in dedication to this principle. "I never wanted to become a buddha or a god," said Professor Cheng not long before he passed away, "I only wanted to be a man." He devoted his life to Confucian ideals and to establishing a bridge between the ancient culture of his native China and the West.

Kong Zi (Confucius), by Tang Dynasty painter Wu Dao Zi. Stone carving in the collection of the Beijing Confucian Temple.

Because the Confucian school focused primarily on self cultivation in terms of benevolence and humanism, expressions of the arcane metaphysical and esoteric aspects of *qì* are rather limited in Confucian texts. Nevertheless, such expressions do appear and, as pointed out by Ezra Pound in his unique translations of the Confucian classics, these constitute a profound if subtle metaphysics. Whereas the Daoists concentrated on accumulating and cultivating the *qì* to attain immortality, the Confucians sought to rectify the *qì* of humankind and subordinate it to the rational social order or *lǐ* 理 as expressed in the rites handed down from generation to generation since antiquity.

This is perhaps why the Confucian school predominated throughout most of Chinese history as the most influential school of thought. Lao Zi's esoteric magic was difficult if not impossible for either an emperor or a common citizen to grasp. Indeed, Lao Zi himself had grown tired of the ways of men and retired from civilization altogether. Confucius, to the contrary, spent his entire life trying to engage the affairs of state. It is one of the great ironies of history that this greatest and most influential of the ancient sages of China spent most of his lifetime as an unemployed wanderer, attended only by a small band of dedicated students, moving from state to state unable to find a monarch who would grant him a long-term governmental position. Were it not for these disciples, we would know nothing at all of the Master's teachings. Like Socrates, his counterpart in the Golden Age of ancient Greece, Confucius himself never wrote one word that survived him. What has accumulated throughout the twenty-five centuries since the end of his recorded life are the transcriptions of this great teacher's oral teachings, along with copious commentaries from disciples of later ages.

Most notable among these latter day commentators of the Confucian school is the great Song Dynasty scholar Zhu Xi. It is to Zhu Xi that we owe the arrangement of the four Confucian classics (*Sì Shū*) 四書: *The Great Learning (Dà Xué)* 大學; *The Doctrine of the Mean* (*Zhōng Yōng*) 中庸 (alternately known as *The Unwobbling Pivot*); *The Analects* (*Lùn Yǔ*) 論語; and the text that bears the name of Confucius' disciple, *Meng Zi (Mèng Zǐ)* 孟子 (Mencius).

Zhu Xi

Zhu Xi was the leading spokesman of the school of thought known today as the "Rationalists" or the "Objective Materialists" that flourished during the Song Dynasty. The Song was a turbulent period in Chinese history, characterized by political strife, Mongol invasions, countless wars of both small and large scale, and an enormous codification and application of what was then already a vast accumulation of traditional arts and sciences. Medicine, mathematics, astronomy, agriculture, technology in general, and especially printing all underwent long and virtually unprecedented periods of development during the reign of the Song. Philosophy lead the way.

Zhu Xi was at the vanguard of intellectuals who charted a course for China during the Song Dynasty. Like many such visionaries and intellectuals, Zhu Xi's work was not immediately accepted. In fact during his lifetime, his work was officially scorned. It was not until long after his death, near the end of the 13th century, that his codification of heavenly rationalism was adopted as an educational standard in the Yuan court which posthumously bestowed upon Zhu Xi his first official government position.[9]

By the beginning of the Ming Dynasty, the crux of the Chinese civil service examination consisted of questions designed to determine applicants' understanding of Zhu Xi's commentaries on the four books of Confucianism and the five ancient Chinese classics. His work remained a central focus of the Chinese intellectual establishment throughout the Ming and Qing Dynasties. To this day, the prevailing impressions of "Confucian" thought are those purveyed by Zhu Xi and his followers.

In a work entitled *Chinese Confucianism* (*Zhōng Guó Rú Xué*)[10] we read:

> *His [Zhu Xi's] systematic rationalism became the official philosophy studied by rulers of China for 700 years. In death, he himself can be compared to Kong [Zi] and Meng [Zi] . . . The kernel of this systematic philosophy is the theory of Heavenly Rationalism, tiān lǐ 天理. The theory of Rationalism and qì is the central concept of this philosophy.*

Zhu Xi postulated that the root of creation was this principle or rationale: *lǐ* 理. In his epistemology, therefore, *lǐ* precedes *qì*. However, echoes of the relationship of *yīn yáng* and *qì* can be sensed in Zhu Xi's thinking. In the first volume of his *Quotations and References of Zhu Zi* (*Zhū Zǐ Yǔ Lèi*), he wrote:

> *There is no qì without lǐ. Yet neither is there lǐ without qì. If somebody asks, "So there must be lǐ first and then qì; is that not right?" the answer must be, "Originally there was no discussion about which came first or second. Yet if the desire to trace*

[9] It is a long-established tradition in China for the dead whose work has posthumously come into favor with the ruling power to be granted such official positions. Lao Zi has been crowned with numerous titles and positions throughout Chinese history.

[10] Xie Xiang Hao, Liu Zong Xian, Sichuan People's Press, 1993.

back their origins must be satisfied, then we would have to say that lǐ holds the primary position. However, [the primary position of] lǐ does not imply that it is independent or, indeed, something other than qì. It exists within qì. If there is no qì, then lǐ has nothing to which it can connect.

In other words, *lǐ* is the implicate order we observe in the manifestations of *qì*, the order that emerges from chaos as a principal feature of existence. *Qì* is thus the fact and the force of this emergence. He clarified the relationship between *lǐ* and *qì* in Volume 58 of his *Collected Writings (Wén Jí)*:

Between heaven and earth there is lǐ and qì. Lǐ is the dào of metaphysics. It is the root that gives birth to matter. Qì is the utensil of physics. It is the tool for giving birth to matter. Though life gives birth to humans and other creatures, they must be endowed with lǐ. Then they have their individual intrinsic natures. They must also be endowed with qì. Then each has its unique shape. Nature and shape, though, even within one single body, reflect a clear differentiation between the dào, lǐ, and the utensil, qì. These must not be confused.

Zhu Xi was a true eclectic. He gathered what he found useful from all available sources. By the Song Dynasty, the accumulation of ancient wisdom was extensive in China. In his *Questions of the Great Learning (Dà Xué Huò Wèn)*, there is evidence of his research into Daoist sources.

The dào of heaven circulates forcefully. It gives birth and support to the ten thousand things. Thus, the creator of All is simply yīn yáng 陰陽 *and wǔ xíng* 五行 *[the five phases]. However, what we know as yīn yáng and the five phases must also follow the law of lǐ for qì to come about. Thus, it is the same for all things in creation. They result from the gathering of qì, thus they have shape and form. Therefore, the birth of man and all other creatures and all matter requires the receipt of lǐ. Only then can health, obedience, benevolence, justice, the rites, and wisdom come into being. Thus for there to be birth, the qì must also connect. Then the body will have a soul, five internal organs, and the hundred bones.*

In Zhu Xi's philosophy, creation was the result of the mingling of *lǐ* and *qì*. This was indeed a mingling of the philosophy of the *dào* with the concept of implicit rational order of creation and society that is contained in the writings of Confucius. Zhu Xi used the concept of rational order to explain the intricacies of *yīn* and *yáng*. In his *Collected Writings*, Volume 50, he wrote:

Generally speaking, yīn and yáng are just one qì. When yīn qì circulates forcefully, it becomes yáng. When yáng qì congeals and consolidates, it becomes yīn. This is not to say, however, that these two are contrary matters.

There are literally hundreds of references to *qì* and its all-important relationship with the rational principle of all existence in the collected works of Zhu Xi. What is perhaps of the greatest significance in the work of Zhu Xi is the intellectual codification of the concept of *qì*. This granted it a virtually permanent place in the realm of Chinese scholarship. What his expressions concerning the nature of *qì* lack in the way of the Daoists' esoteric mysticism and mystery, they more than replace by establishing *qì* as a cornerstone in the foundation of Chinese thinking. For more than 600 years, every Mandarin who held an official position in China had to compose essays that evidenced complete familiarity with, and understanding of, the relationship between *qì* and *lĭ*. For the past six centuries China has been guided by scholars who shared a common understanding of the nature of *qì* and the role it played in both the natural world and the world of civil affairs.

In no small part, it was Zhu Xi's iteration of the relationship between *lĭ* and *qì* that made this philosophy so acceptable to Chinese rulers. The concept of *lĭ* is inseparably linked to the great chain of existence that begins in heaven and establishes the emperor as the Son of Heaven. *Qì*, on the other hand, vibrates with the chaotic vigor of the natural world. It was the rationalism of Zhu Xi that brought the natural force of *qì* under the control and command of the Chinese orthodoxy—or so they were able to believe, citing Zhu Xi and his followers as their authority.

Section Five: The Influence of *Qì* in Western Philosophy: Leibniz, Bohr, and Contemporary Theorists

The influence of the life and work of the great Danish physicist Niels Bohr is equaled by few other individuals of the 20th century. Perhaps only Albert Einstein's epochal theory of relativity surpasses Bohr's contributions. Niels Bohr established the science of quantum mechanics. At the heart of Bohr's theoretical description of the essence of matter and the universe is the dual nature of reality at the sub-atomic level. One look at the coat of arms which

Niels Bohr's coat of arms.

Yīn yáng symbol (*tài jí tú*).

Bohr designed for himself and his heirs reveals what to many may seem a surprising source from which this esteemed scientist drew inspiration. Here we see one of the most curious and significant manifestations of the symbol of *yīn* and *yáng* outside of its native China.

An obvious and compelling question: Why does the diagram known for thousands of years in China as *tài jí tú* occupy a central position in the thoughts of the esteemed grandfather of modern physics? Clearly, Bohr was able to see the correlation between the philosophy of the *dào* and the structure of matter through the perspective of quantum mechanics. Bohr gathered from his study of Daoism that "on the stage of life we are both actors and audience." The *tài jí* diagram left a lasting impression on this great mind that gave the world of physics the theory of complementarity on which quantum mechanics is based. An even more interesting and provocative fact is that the concept of *yīn* and *yáng*, and with it the concept of *qì*, have played a role of central and seminal importance in the development of Western scientific thought since it was first introduced to Western Europe at the end of the seventeenth century.

Arriving in China during the Ming Dynasty (1368 C.E.–1644 C.E.), Jesuit and Franciscan missionaries were the first Western Europeans to systematically study and translate the classical books of ancient China. The Golden Age of Chinese civilization had already passed during the Tang Dynasty (618 C.E.–907 C.E.). The intervening Song Dynasty was a period of extensive synthesis and integration of intellectual and scientific principles. China had also been successfully invaded by *nú zhēn* nationals (Mongols) who established the Yuan Dynasty (1279 C.E.–1368 C.E.) that lasted for nearly 100 years.

All of this had come to pass before the first Franciscans and Jesuits stepped upon Chinese shores. Thus, what these early religious explorers discovered was an intellectual milieu characterized by the efforts of Chinese scholars to resurrect the glory of bygone days. Perhaps the prevailing intellectual bias was that of the Neo-Confucianists (otherwise known as the Objective Materialists) of the Song Dynasty. This Neo-Confucian school was a blend of several traditions of Chinese philosophy and scholarship including primarily Daoist but also Confucian attributes. As we noted in the previous section, the most well known of the Neo-Confucians was the Song philosopher Zhu Xi.

Why is it important to grasp this Chinese philosophical history? Ever since the beginning of the imperial era of Chinese history at the establishment of the Qin Dynasty (221 B.C.E.–207 B.C.E.), there has been a prominent tendency for those in positions of power to reinterpret and, in fact, to reinvent the past. The first emperor of China attempted to do this in grand fashion by collecting all the books in the empire and, with few exceptions, setting them ablaze. He is said to have ordered the great majority of scholars and intellectuals to be buried alive, leaving only their heads above ground. Thus those officials left to record history could look into their dying eyes as their ideas perished with them, an unmistakable warning as to what would and would not be permitted to survive.

There is no absolute certainty concerning the textual "originals" these Franciscan and Jesuit monks were offered as authoritative. No doubt the materials they were given were strongly influenced by the the Neo-Confucians, as their influence was still strong during the Ming. Such considerations open the door to considerable speculation and provide a sense of the complexity involved in studying China's long and convoluted past. In Joseph Campbell's words:

> *. . . all of the myths (or rather as we now have them, moralizing anecdotes) of the Chinese golden age have to be recognized as the productions rather of a Confucian forest of pencils than any 'good earth' or 'forest primeval.' And, if gems or jades are to be found among them for the actual mythology of Yangshao, Lungshan [Longshan], Shang, or even Chou [Zhou] (anything earlier, that is to say, than Shih Huang Ti's [Shi Huang Di's] burning of the books, 213 B.C.), we have to realize that they have been lifted from the primitive, and remounted carefully in a late, highly sophisticated setting, like an old Egyptian scarab mounted as a ring for some fine lady's hand.*

What arrived in the cultural centers of Western Europe through the agency of these learned priests was a distinct and quite naturally biased impression of Chinese philosophy and religion. One of the most enthusiastic recipients of such materials was the great German philosopher and mathematician Gottfried Wilhelm von Leibniz.

Gottfried Wilhelm von Leibniz

In the late seventeenth century, Leibniz was living in Paris. He was already famous throughout Europe. He had authored a philosophical monograph entitled "Le Monadologie" which many see as the seminal germ of the organic philosophy of science that has predominated in Western scientific circles virtually ever since. He published a form of calculus and argued with the great English mathematician and father of physics, Newton, over who was the inventor of that discipline. He also, without dispute, created another form of mathematical computation which has since become very important: binary notation.

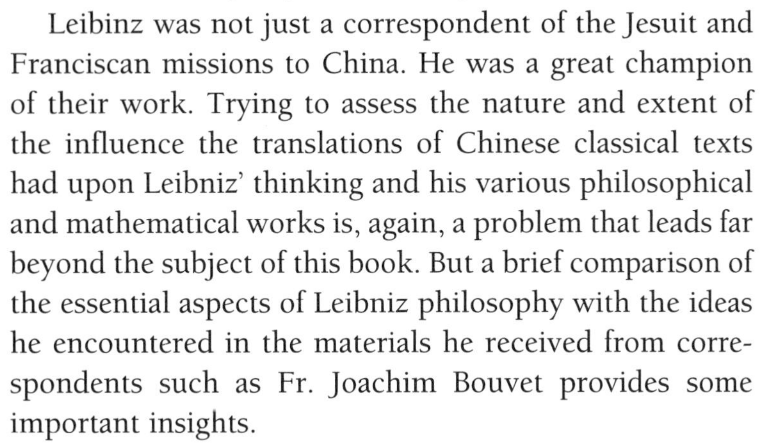

Leibinz was not just a correspondent of the Jesuit and Franciscan missions to China. He was a great champion of their work. Trying to assess the nature and extent of the influence the translations of Chinese classical texts had upon Leibniz' thinking and his various philosophical and mathematical works is, again, a problem that leads far beyond the subject of this book. But a brief comparison of the essential aspects of Leibniz philosophy with the ideas he encountered in the materials he received from correspondents such as Fr. Joachim Bouvet provides some important insights.

Bouvet sent Leibniz a translation of the most ancient of all Chinese classics, the *Book of Changes* (*Yì Jīng*) 易經. The *Yì Jīng* is the quintessential expression of a mathematically derived and metaphorically interpreted description of the relationships of *yīn* and *yáng*. It is an ancient binary computer that has been used throughout Chinese history as a device for predicting the future, interpreting the past, and dispensing kernels of wisdom to those who fathom its deceptively simple images. These poetic images led students of the *Yì Jīng* into chasms of philosophy that opened onto vast mathematical vistas. They led some of the European monks, who devoted decades trying to understand these images, to commit suicide. Even today in China, scholars approach the study of the *Yì Jīng* with tremendous respect and some temerity. Like the holy books of other ancient traditions, the *Yì Jīng* is believed by some to contain the key to all creation.

Regardless of the truth of such beliefs, what the *Book of Changes* indisputably contains is a mathematical algorithm for the complex pattern of changes deriving from the interplay of *yīn* and *yáng*. As we explained in the preceding sections, the chief descriptive term for this interplay of *yīn* and *yáng* is "*qì*." *Qì* is the manifestation that results from every transformation that can be expressed in terms of *yīn* and *yáng*.

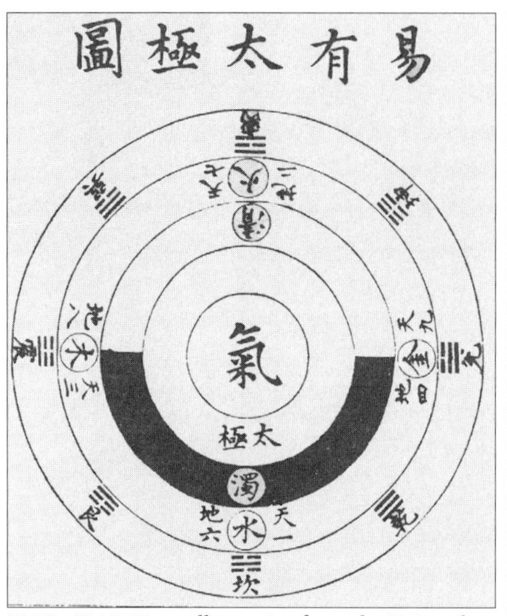

Yī Yǒu Tài Jí Tú, an illustration from the *Yì Jīng* that places *qì* at the center. From *Chéng Shì Mò Yuán*, a Ming Dynasty collection of ink block prints.

Yet the function of *qì* in the scheme of *yīn* and *yáng* may well have been lost on Leibniz. In Leibniz' binary mathematics we see a clear and distinct impression of the ancient dialectics of the Chinese sages. Yet like the reflection in a fun house mirror, the image is distorted. What Leibniz and Bohr beheld in the Chinese concepts of *yīn* and *yáng* was nothing other than the creative power of *qì*. These two great minds were not unique among Western thinkers who have found among ancient Chinese sources inspiration concerning basic issues of disciplines such as mathematics and physics.

In 1789 the French chemist Lavoisier wrote the following sentence which suggests a haunting influence of *yīn yáng* theory. In fact, it reads like a passage from the ancient Chinese classics of *yīn yáng* and *dào*: "The total of the substance congealed in the universe is unchangeable." Compare this to Zhuang Zi's remark, "In all the world there is but one *Qì*."

Lavoisier conducted a famous series of experiments which consisted of burning coal then collecting and weighing the byproducts. Contrary to the then current paradigm of phlogistic chemistry, the coal was not destroyed as it burned. The substances he collected and weighed from the burning coal were heavier than the original sample. Nothing had been lost. In fact, something had been acquired. This acquisition was, Lavoisier realized, the oxygen that combined with the carbon during the process he therefore named "oxidation." This was an enormous breakthrough in the history of Western science. In fact, it launched the modern discipline of chemistry and fairly well defined what has come to be known as the Second Law of Thermodynamics: neither matter nor energy can be created or destroyed. All the various changes to which matter and energy are subject are merely changes in state.

Despite the fact that this understanding is historically attributed as a "discovery" of eighteenth century Europe, it had been known for millennia in China. In fact it was precisely such an understanding that was contained in the translations of Chinese classics which the Jesuits and Franciscans of the 17th century exported from China to be studied by European cognoscenti of the day. Is it merely coincidence that this sort of scientific breakthrough occurred in Europe within decades of the introduction of *yīn yáng* theory from China?

A look at more recent work published in these fields reveals a growing awareness among Western scientists that ancient Chinese thinkers not only anticipated contemporary problems but postulated a series of rational answers. Fritjof Capra's *Tao of Physics* is an early example of a work that explores the ancient antecedents of the two-fold nature of reality as it is currently understood. In the 1970s another book attempted to summarize then-current trends as a confluence of ancient Chinese and contemporary Western views of the forces that stitch together the fabric of the universe. *The Dancing Wu Li Masters,* by Gary Zukav, reports on the work of contemporary researchers who search for the ultimate particle of matter and for a unified field theory to explain the interrelationships between them. As Zukav points out, these modern researchers find themselves in territory that is remarkably similar to the one described in Daoist texts more than 2000 years ago. It seems quite natural that many have been led to the same conclusions Daoist sages put forward in these ancient passages.

One way of describing books such as the *Dào Dé Jīng* is to compare them to modern handbooks, manuals that contain the essential theories and techniques that one needs to know in order to operate a particular system. The system in question is the one we know as consciousness, the one that brings us the experience of life. That is to say that the Chinese realized thousands of years ago that the human mind is an artifact that must be studied and that the capacities we know as perception and cognition are in fact skills, the essential art from which all others derive.

To acquire and refine such skills, the presence of *qì*, a force arising from the interplay of universal, complimentary opposites that the Chinese have described for thousands of years as *yīn* and *yáng*, is an unquestionably essential aspect of the universe in which we live.

Chapter 3

Qì in the Arts

It is this spirit of calm and harmony, this flavor of the mountain air (shan lin ch'i) always a little tinged with the recluse's passion for leisure and solitude, which characterizes all forms of Chinese art. Consequently, its characteristic is not supremacy over nature but harmony with nature.

—*Lin Yu Tang, My Country, My People*

Recent archaeological discoveries have led to a reevaluation of the antiquity of civilization and culture in China. What has long been referred to as over five thousand years of continuous cultural development is now considered as a span of at least ten thousand years. Throughout these hundred centuries, Chinese artists and craftspeople have been making art that embodies and celebrates their ideas and experiences. Ancient artifacts are constantly being unearthed and added to museum collections where they stand in silent yet eloquent testimony to the genius of China's past masters.

People from every part of the world have marveled at the unique styles of artistic expression they behold in Chinese paintings, ceramics, poetry, dance, and music. Yet for many in the West, the complex meanings of such work are hard to decipher. During the course of our research for this book, we followed the common thread that runs through the artwork of virtually every age of China's long past. This thread continues to wend its way into the fabric of artistic and cultural life in China today. Indeed, many of the artists, art historians, and critics of art with whom we have spoken, and whose work we have seen and read over the past several years, mention this single conceptual thread as the most important element in Chinese art. This thread is *qì*.

Section One: The Momentum of Qì— *Yī Qì Hē Chéng*

Chinese art emphasizes the expression of motion and strength. This vital dynamism has various identifying characteristics that reflect the philosophical constructs mentioned in the preceding chapter. It arises from the ancient dialectical unity: substantial and insubstantial; movement and stillness; firmness and softness; gathering and dispersal. This dialectical construction is easily recognized in terms of Chinese philosophy as *yīn* and *yáng*. In Chinese painting it manifests in wholeness; the entirety of the composition tends "to configure the whole world on one foot of the scroll. It manifests as a momentum containing heaven and earth and the whole universe."[1]

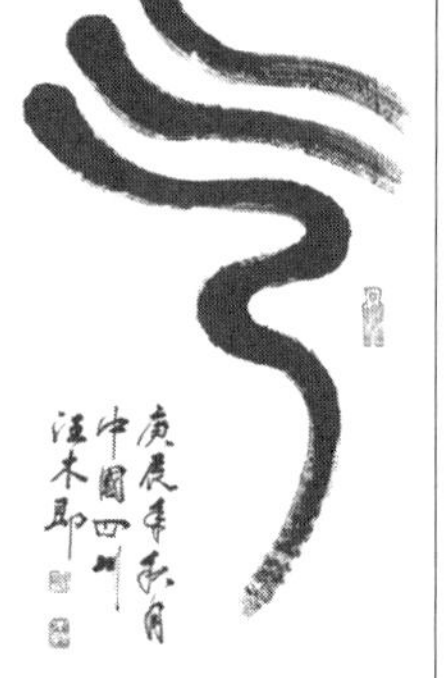

Qì Calligraphy by Wang Mu Ji

The tension that holds together this wholeness of composition develops from the most fundamental graphic elements: black and white. This blackness and whiteness, substantiality and insubstantiality, become the internal *qì* of intelligence, the germ of style and character. Hence the whiteness and blackness, insubstantiality and substantiality, contain the *dào* of breathing in and out, the *yīn* and *yáng* of the universe, the *qì* of the highest aspiration surrounding every flowing river. The *dào* of *yīn* and *yáng* and the *qì* of high aspiration combine in a visual effect

[1]Meng Gu, *Transmission of Spirit and Understanding,* Beijing: International Cultural Publishing Co., 1989, p.76.

Luò Shéng, goddess of the Luo River. Painted by Gu Kai Zhi (c 346 C.E-407 C.E.), a great painter of the Jin Dynasty.

that creates a magical power. Anyone nourished and benefited by such traditions of Chinese culture is guided into an integrated understanding of the universe and life.[2] The aesthetic engine, this "magical power," Relies upon *qì* for its fuel and its motive force.

All forms of Chinese art are closely interrelated and integrated by *qì*. The art of calligraphy is driven by "the pulse of *qì*." In painting this pulse develops into "the charm of *qì*." Literary expressions divide into two categories. Prose is motivated by "the momentum of *qì*;" poetry is carried by its "romantic charm." All these factors develop a sense of the beautiful and work on many levels to harmonize the artist, the work of art, and those who behold them together with nature.

酒斟時須
滿十分浮

Calligraphy by Su Dong Po, Song Dynasty.

Nature in Chinese philosophy is understood to be the constant motion that manifests the changes of life. The root of these changes is *qì*. The concept of *qì* is used to explain the generation, development, and transformation of all matter. It holds the premiere position in traditional Chinese thought. Not only is *qì* the principal source of energy and matter, it also establishes the basis of spirit and the human soul. Importantly, it provides the connective medium through which the ancient philosophers

[2] *Ibid.*

believed human beings could harmonize their growth and development with the forces of nature.

This quest for harmony with nature gained its preeminent expression in the philosophy of the *dào*. Yet all this philosophizing can scarcely compete with the experience of a work of art. After all, the idea that one picture is worth a thousand words is intimately Chinese. Thus, throughout the ages, Chinese artists have sought to manifest the *dào* of nature in their lives and in their work. They applied their intellect to comprehend the changes of the natural world and to transform their perception of the *dào* into the emotional power needed to fuel the expression of their art. This emotional vitality, in fact, is their own, individual *qì*.

They strove to cultivate and refine this *qì* so that their work could be created directly from it. This aesthetic yearning for unity and harmony is expressed in the phrase, *yī qì hē chéng* 一 氣 呵 成 which literally means, "one breath of *qì* and it is done." It is used of literary compositions to imply a particular fluidity of the movement of ideas from start to finish—the momentum of *qì*. This concept is not limited to a single discipline or mode of expression. It runs throughout all of Chinese art. In fact, this phrase is commonly used to describe the accomplishment of anything done in one fell swoop, without interruption or pause.

The following passage is from the Confucian classic known as the *Book of Rites (Lǐ Jì)* from the Spring and Autumn Period (770 B.C.E–476 B.C.E). In the volume entitled "Records of Music (*Yuè Jì*)," we read:

> *Poetry is the expression of the will or aspiration. Song is the recitation of sounds. Dance emotes and mobilizes form. These three originate in the heart, aroused by music. Thus deep feelings enlighten writing. It is the flourishing of qì that thus transforms the spirit. Its accumulation and harmonization in the center will draw out the excellence of the spirit. Thus must music be created without the slightest falsity.*

Honesty and righteousness have long been fundamental requirements of Chinese art. They arise from an understanding of the forces involved in the process of artistic creation and reflect the profound roots of morality in Chinese culture. This morality is not based in the Western dichotomy of right versus wrong or good versus evil. It develops from inspection of nature and an understanding of how life should be lived to harmonize human action with the forces of the natural world.

In the Liang period of the Southern Dynasty (502 C.E.–557 C.E.) Zhong Rong expanded upon this ancient theme in a book entitled *Classes of Poetry (Shī Pǐn Xù).*

> *Poetry is an act of will. It comes from the heart. A poem embodies words. The feelings arise from the center and give shape and substance to the words. Language is not enough. To rely on language is to sigh and lament. Sighing and lamenting cannot result in reciting and singing. Even to recite and sing is not enough. Thus we must dance it. This is all to say that the creation of art is guided by the spirit.*

Zhong Rong's work was one of the earliest bodies of literary criticism in China. It focused on the "Five Character" form of poetry in vogue from the Han Dynasty until Zhong's era. His work had an enormous influence on successive generations of writers and readers in China. Through such influence, the movements of *qì* came to be guided by the spirit, informed by a sense of profound moral obligation to achieve balance and natural harmony. These movements drove traditional art in China steadily forward through the ages. The vast and complex tapestry of the traditional arts in China is indeed woven from this one, single thread. To understand the fundamental principles of the movement of *qì* in Chinese art, we begin with an examination of the ancient art of the dance.

Section Two: The Dance of *Qì*

A comment written in 239 B.C.E. includes a vivid explanation of the origin of the art of dance in ancient China. It is contained in *Lu's Annals of Spring and Autumn (Lǚ Shì Chūn Qīu).*

> *In past times at the beginning of the Yin Kang period [during the Xia period, 21st century* B.C.E.*–16th century* B.C.E.*], the yīn qì was obstructed and stagnated. The water pathways [of the earth] were congested and did not freely flow. The qì of humankind became sluggish and gloomy. Peoples' sinews and bones curled with cold and could not extend to their fullest. Thus dancing was created to ward off stagnation.*

This note echoes centuries later in a version of the same history from the Song writer Luo Mi. In Volume Seven of a book entitled *The Path of History (Lù Shǐ)*, it reads as follows:

During the period known as Yin Kang, the water pathway was obstructed. Rivers could not flow from their origins. The yīn congealed and the changes of yīn and yáng closed. Thus the people were gloomy and depressed inside. Their skin was obstructed and most people experienced swellings. Those who knew how to mobilize their joints composed the art of dancing wǔ 舞 and taught the people to dance, allowing the obstruction to be removed, to guide and connect the qì. This was called the "Great Dance."

Seven Plates Dance (rubbing of a Han Dynasty tomb carving.)

Here we see an intimate relationship between medicine and dance in ancient China. We will return to this relationship at the end of this chapter. For now it is important to note that the proto-healers of prehistoric times, the shaman or *wū* 巫 , incorporated dancing and chanting in their healing rituals. Their dance was their medicine. The origins of the character 巫 reveal the intimacy of this relationship. In the oldest extant dictionary of the Chinese language, the *Discussion of Language and Explanation of Characters (Shuō Wén Jiě Zì)*, written in the Han Dynasty circa 100 C.E., the roots of the character for dance are described as follows:

> *Woman can manifest and mobilize Form and thus beckon God and call down heavenly manifestations through the Dance . . . because they can call upon God by dancing, the character appeared to resemble the "long sleeve dance."*[3]

A pictograph of the long sleeves of the dancers' costumes can be seen in the interior portions of the character *gōng* 工. This character means "work." It is, in its own right, a pictograph of a simple tool used for measuring, an ancient T-square. Importantly it is also the scepter-like instrument often pictured in the hands of the Chinese goddess Nu Wa, one of the highest deities in the Chinese pantheon.

Pictograph of the long sleeves of the dancers' costumes.

Long Sleeve Dance. From a rubbing of a Han Dynasty tomb carving.

The dancing *wū* are associated linguistically with both divinity and the healing arts. Dance is also noted in the book entitled *The History of the Art of Chinese Qì Gōng (Zhōng Guó Qì Gōng Shǐ)*, as the origin of *dǎo yǐn* 導引, an early antecedent of *qì gōng*. Thus we see that the mobilization of *qì* through dancing is an ancient source of many cultural movements that are still vital activities in China today. (See Chapter 5 for a more complete discussion of *dǎo yǐn* and *qì gōng*.)

Personal stamps from the shamans—relating to the character *gōng*.

[3] The "long sleeve dance" is a very ancient and still popular form of dance in China. The costumes include sleeves that are exaggeratedly long, extending as much as a meter beyond the hands.

The relationship between *qì* and dance becomes even clearer when the historical development of the art of dancing is considered. In ancient times dance was known as the art that "mobilized form." When bodies danced, the changes of *qì* became manifest and visible. Thus the spirit could express itself directly through bodily movement. This spiritual expression was recognized as possessing healing power. It also possessed the "charm of *qì*" and could thus influence not only the human spirit but also those unseen spirits believed to play an essential role in causing disease. Thus, as the ancient shamans danced over and around their patients, they became powerful, knowledgeable, the "great ones."

Nu Wa

A shaman (*wū*) prepares an herbal medication for a prince (the soul) to assist his journey. (Rubbing of a Han Dynasty tomb carving.)

The art of dancing established its place in the foundation of Chinese civilization. As the great Spanish mystic, St. John of the Cross, stated succinctly hundreds of years later and half a world away, "Whoso danceth not knoweth not what cometh to pass."

Entertainment. From a rubbing of a Han Dynasty tomb carving.

An examination of the derivation of the English word "art" reveals yet another close correlation between the ancient Chinese and Greek conceptions of the source of artistic vitality. The English word, "art," comes directly from Latin "ars." "Ars," however, is the romanization of a Greek word, "artos." This Greek word, far from meaning "art," means "joint." It is the root of the word "arthritis," the "inflammation of the joints." What at first glance appears to be a huge conceptual gap is quickly closed when it is understood that the Latin "ars" was a shortened borrowing from a Greek phrase, "artos tekne" meaning "the skill of the joints." The Greek word "tekne" meaning "skill," is found as the roots of English words such as "technique" and "technology."

The Greek phrase *artos tekne* is from ancient Greek art. It pertained especially to the skills of the sculptor for whom a primary concern was the faithful reproduction of the human joints. After all, without our joints, we humans would be immobile masses of flesh and bones. For the sculptor, the dancer, indeed for any artist in any form of art that deals with the human form, the function and appearance of the joints is of fundamental importance in expressing the vitality of life and art. Thus the Greek phrase, *artos tekne*, "the skill of the joints," shortened into Latin as *ars,* and arrived centuries later in English as "art."

Compare the quotation cited above from Luo Mi of the Song Dynasty, "Those who knew how to mobilize their joints composed the art of dancing and taught the people to dance . . ." Perhaps the ancient world was a smaller and better connected place than anyone has yet found scientific evidence to prove. If such evidence exists, perhaps it is to be found in the dancing traces of the *qì* of ancient artists.

SECTION THREE: *QÌ* IN THE EDUCATION AND TRAINING OF ARTISTS: THE BASIS OF AESTHETIC STANDARDS

Bai Ju Yi, one of the greatest literary figures of the Tang Dynasty (618 C.E. –907 C.E.), wrote:

> *There is a pure qì of intelligence existing between heaven and earth.*
> *Every form of life receives it, but humans receive the most.*

He explained that it was the role, and indeed the responsibility of writers to refine and congeal this *qì* so that it could be guided by the will, released and disseminated as literature. Thus, throughout Chinese history many of the great artists, writers, and musicians were also practitioners of *qì gōng*, a form of exercise to accumulate, cultivate, and refine the *qì*. [See Chapter 5 for a lengthier discussion of the nature of *qì gōng*.]

The reason is simple. *Qì* has long been understood as the motive force of life itself. Powerful and unseen, it drives all natural phenomena. Traditional arts in China are dominated by themes drawn from the natural environment. Thus artists in China trained themselves not just in techniques that would allow them to replicate the forms and images of the natural world but in methods of acquiring a deep understanding of the essence of such phenomena and of the forces that bring them to life. They practiced to increase their own spirit and personal *qì* and to enable themselves to connect more thoroughly with nature. They thus became conduits of this motive force, so that the lifeblood of their art might become indistinguishable from the vast *qì* of nature. Such cultivation was the bedrock on which the foundations of Chinese art were established.

Liu Xi Zai of the Qing Dynasty (1644 C.E.–1911 C.E.) made this clear. In his book *Conception of Art (Yì Gài),* there is a discourse titled "Treatise on the Conception of Calligraphy (*Shū Gài*):"

The best is to cultivate the shén [spirit].
Next is to cultivate the qì.
Last of all is to cultivate the form.

Again and again this is made clear by Chinese artists and writers throughout history. Su Che, a scholar of the Song Dynasty, wrote:

Literature is shaped by qì. Yet the ability to write does not derive from slavish devotion. Only by relying on qì can [the writer] achieve perseverance.

He cited two methods of "relying on *qì*." One was to follow the advice of Meng Zi and preserve one's righteous *qì*—to cultivate an upright spirit. The other was to heed the words of the great historian and author of the *Book of History (Shǐ Jì)*, Si Ma Qian:

To become aware of the outer world, to connect with nature, you must travel. See the marvels and natural phenomena. If you can accomplish this, the qì will fill up the center of your being. It will overflow into your face. It will arouse your speech, inspire and manifest in your writing without your even noticing.

The appearance of *qì* in literary compositions, particularly poetry, was considered of primary importance. The fundamental imagistic character of Chinese poetry developed from this consideration as expressed in the words of Liu Xi Zai:

The spirit of the mountain cannot express itself, thus it emerges through writing the mists and clouds in the twilight. The spirit of the Spring cannot be expressed in words, but it is revealed in grass and trees. Therefore, if the poem contains no appearance of qì [i.e., no image] then the spirit will have no dwelling place.

The appearance of *qì* is the basis of poetic imagery, but only through the cultivation of *qì* can these images naturally emerge. The point is driven home by the comments of the Qing Dynasty (1644 C.E.–1911 C.E.) poet, Zheng Zhen.

It is good to read and study many books. But especially precious is the cultivation of the righteous qì. Only when the qì is upright does my self truly exist. Only then can the erudition gained from study attain its full and mutual benefit.[4]

[4] Quoted from *The Journal of Eastern Qì Gōng*, Vol X, No. X.

The conception of Chinese art is not rooted in reproducing images of the objective world. Rather, Chinese artists sought to cast themselves, their individual understanding of the world, their feelings, and their spirit into their compositions. The training of the artist thus relied first and foremost upon the development of an understanding of *qì* and of techniques for accumulating *qì* so that it could be released and expressed through the work of art. This is not to suggest that the training in specific technical skills was of secondary importance, rather that the acquisition of technical expertise has always been understood to be utterly inseparable from the acquisition of *qì*. This understanding served not only as the basis of artistic discipline and training but of standards of aesthetic judgment.

Xie Zhen of the Ming Dynasty expressed the gist of this aesthetic standard in *A Discussion of the Poetry of the Four Seas (Sì Míng Shī Huà)*: "If poetry lacks *shén qì*, it is like a drawing of the sun and moon without light."

Xià Shān Gāo Yǐn Tú (Dwelling in the Summer Mountain) by Wang Meng of the Yuan dynasty. In the collection of the Beijing Imperial Palace Museum.

Section Four: The Charm of *Qì*

In one of the oldest extant discussions of painting entitled *Records of the Painting of Yun Tai Mountain (Huà Yún Tái Shān Jì)*, Gu Kai Zhi, one of the greatest painter of the Jin Dynasty (317 C.E.–420 C.E.), wrote:

> *When painting the Heavenly Master, you must neglect his figure and concentrate on drawing out the qì of his spirit . . . There runs the stream from bottom up; the perspective of objective things turns everything upside down. Pure qì brings down the mountains! This is the method of painting the mountain.*[5]

Qì has always figured prominently in the methodology of Chinese art. The Southern Qi period (479 C.E.–502 C.E.) witnessed the introduction of the Six Methods as the "key to painting."

[5]From Li Qing, *The Point of View of Man in Chinese Culture,* Xue Lin Publishing House, Shanghai, 1996.

The first to present a systematic summary of traditional Chinese painting at this time was Xie He in a work entitled *Records of the Character of Ancient Painting (Gŭ Pĭn Huà Lù).* The foremost of the six methods he recorded was "feeling the charm of *qì*." This theory of "the charm of *qì*" became a cornerstone in the foundations of traditional Chinese painting. Writing in the Tang Dynasty (618 C.E.–907 C.E.) in *Records of Famous Paintings from throughout the Dynasties* (*Lì Dài Míng Huà Jì*), Zhang Yan Yuan noted:

> *Ancient painting can transform action directly from form yet still uphold the bones of qì.*[6] *Seek the painting out of the form. This is difficult to explain to lay people. Contemporary painting, though possessed of form, lacks the charm of qì. Therefore, utilize the charm of qì to accomplish the composition of painting, and the form will be implicit.*

Hán Jiang Dú Diào Tú (Fishing in Solitude on Cold River) by Ma Yuan of the Southern Song Dynasty. In the Collection of the Taibei Imperial Palace Museum.

What is the "charm of *qì*?" In the Qing Dynasty, Zhang Geng explained it in a book called *A Discussion of Painting from Lu Mountain (Lú Shān Huà Lùn).*

> *There is the charm of qì, transmitted via the ink, some via the brush, some through action without intention. The highest level is that transmitted through actions with no intention. The next is action with intention. The next is that which is transmitted through the brush. The lowest is that sent through the ink.*
>
> *What does it mean to send it through the ink? It means the painting is accomplished by spreading the ink like a halo around the sketched-out drawing. What is it that is called transmitted via the brush? It means the use of the dry brush to rub out the light ink strokes with thorough strength so that light itself flows out.*

---

[6]The phrase "bones of *qì*" is a literal translation of the Chinese expression *gŭ qì*. This is an idiomatic, technical term in the nomenclature of traditional Chinese fine arts. It has several meanings that derive from the figurative juxtaposition of these two words. One common meaning of this phrase is "spirit." In painting, however, it refers to the formal aspect of a composition, i.e., to the spirit that holds a composition together, in place.

What is meant by action with intention? It means the artist can liberate the method of using the brush and the movement of ink so that they correspond to whatever the intention is: sparse or dense; varied amounts; thick or light; dry or moist. All can exist in perfect arrangement.

What is meant by action without intention? It means the artist fixes his attention and concentration, and then the vision flows out through the movements of the wrist. The original intention is one thing, but suddenly it appears completely different! It comes out just like that, sent out with no intention. You can say, "It is enough." But in fact it is not enough. How can you call it enough, when there is no way to add it up? It is originality beyond the feelings of the brush and the weight of the ink. It comes from the thriving pivot of heaven. Yet it can only be sensed by one who is tranquil. Even the slightest delay will confuse the mind, and it disappears in the ink.

It is indeed no easy matter to understand this concept, for first one must grasp the answer to a more basic question: what is *qì*? The heft of this book in your hand is to some extent a measure of the import of the latter question. If *qì* could be understood in a single word or phrase, it would not take such an effort to describe and define it. Of course, to the Chinese, *qì* is *qì*. It needs no further explanation unless one seeks to fathom the depths of its mysteries and, indeed, the charms that have grown around this deceptively simple word. To understand the charm of *qì*, we must look into these depths.

In ancient times, primitive people did not create elaborate explanations for the phenomena of the natural world. The wind blew across the face of the earth. Rain fell. Thunder and lightning came, startling all far and wide. The sun rose and fell, exchanging its place at the zenith with the moon following its own, unique patterns. The explanations that ancient Chinese evolved for such phenomena all partook of the concept of *qì*. In time a group of magicians and shamans, the *wū*, developed. They occupied the position between the forces of the natural world and human beings. These shamans developed the ability to "control and utilize *qì*" through mobilizing and sublimating not only the *qì* of natural phenomena, but also the *qì* of supernatural beings, invisible spirits, and demons.

To exert this control over the *qì* of nature and to intervene between humans and supernatural forces, these shaman used the archetypal tools of magical correspondences: chants and incantations, dancing, and various elaborate rituals, combined with potions concocted from the roots and leaves of plants mixed together with the severed parts of animals. All these efforts were undertaken to influence, that is, to charm people and to induce their belief in the power of the shaman. The natural result was that people came to have faith in their magical abilities.

As the centuries passed and ancient superstitions began to give way to more articulate, technical explanations of natural phenomena and the forces that afflicted people, the shaman began to disappear. This evolution occurred with and fed back upon the evolution from magical correspondences to the notion of systematic correspondences; and the *wū* thus evolved to become counselors, mathematicians, physicians, alchemists and chemists, astronomers, engineers, and the entire spectrum of intellectuals and artisans. Some *wū* remained and their practices continue until today, although they are submerged in the countryside beneath the mainstream of modern culture. The concept of *qì*, however, endured all these transformations. Some would say that it was *qì* that engendered such growth and development. Thus some of the flavor of the ancient, magic world was retained within the concept of *qì* itself. To this day in China, as elsewhere, there are those who understand *qì* as a supernatural force. As this concept has spread to other cultures, however, it is today heavily overlaid with the belief systems of the recipient culture, whether largely biblical concepts of "spirit" or the popular if ill-defined concept of "energy."

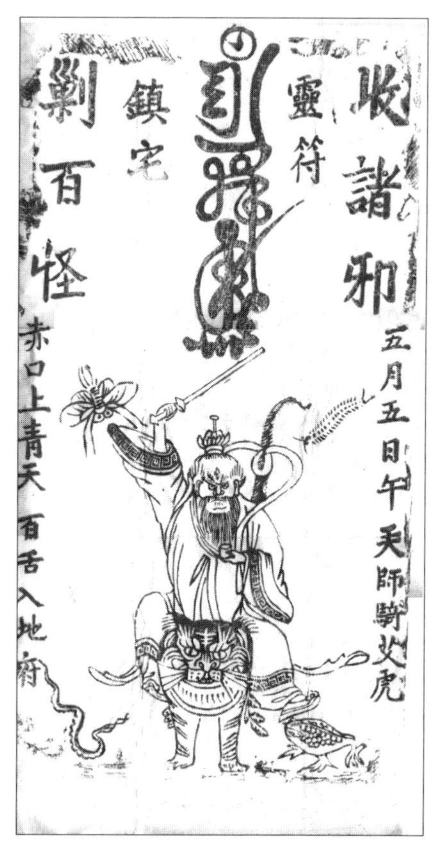

Charm from Qing Cheng Mountain.

We cannot say with certainty how widespread such beliefs are in the contemporary world, although even if the percentage is small, there may still be millions of Chinese who conceive of *qì* as a powerful force capable of producing extraordinary, even miraculous effects. Moreover, for a great majority of the Chinese people, *qì* is a cultural motif that has moved civilization steadily forward on the grandest scale. The flow of *qì* has carved a deep, indelible impression in the Chinese psyche over the millennia. It resonates in every aspect of Chinese life.

The charm of *qì* is a rarefied and cultivated harmonic of this fundamental resonance. Yet it still retains some of the primordial flavor described above. That is to say that in the hands of a master of traditional Chinese painting, a single stroke of the brush, imbued with the charm of *qì*, transports the spirit of those who view its traces. People viewing Chinese paintings created many centuries ago experience this charm of *qì*, whether they are Chinese or strangers in lands far removed from the yellow earth of China. This is a manifestation of the harmony of the internal and external worlds, the world of objects and the world of the spirit. The charm of *qì* is the shuttle that weaves back and forth to bring about this harmony. In the Tang Dynasty, Zhang Yan Yuan stated this clearly: "Seek the painting in the charm of *qì*; then the resemblances of form are woven within."

The relative importance of *qì* and its charm was explicitly described in the Five Dynasties period (907 C.E.–960 C.E.) by Jing Hao who wrote of the six keys to skill in a work entitled *Records of the Methods of the Brush (Bǐ Fǎ Jì):*

First is Qì.
Second is Charm.
Third is Mind.
Fourth is View.
Fifth is Line.
Sixth is Ink.

Later in the Song Dynasty the great authority of Chinese artistic criticism, Guo Ruo Xu, elaborated on the significance and relative importance of these six keys or methods of traditional painting in his *Records of the Knowledge of Painting (Tú Huà Jiàn Wén Jì):*

> *The discussion of the six methods of painting will never change for ten thousand years. From the "bone method"*[7] *(gǔ fǎ* 骨法*) of using the brush on down, five of these methods can be learned through study. Only the charm of qì comes from innate intelligence. It is the feeling of elegance that endows painting. Since the moral character of a*

[7]The "bone method" (*gǔ fǎ*) is an aspect of how to use the brush to construct the composition of a painting.

painter must be high, the charm of qì must be of a high level. Attaining a high level of the charm of qì, motion emerges [in the painting]. This is the so-called spirit of the spirit that enables [one] to connect with the essence.

In his *Discussion of Famous Paintings from throughout the Dynasties (Lì Dài Míng Huà Jì)*, Zhang Yan Yuan emphasized this point again and again:

> *The mind comes before the brush. The mind remains even after the painting is complete. This completeness is the qì of the spirit.*

According to contemporary scholar Meng Gu, in his *Transmission of Spirit and Understanding (Shén Yǔ Wù Dé Chuán Dòng)*, "The profound purpose in Chinese painting is tranquility."

The highest praise for the poetry of the ancients is "there is a painting in the poem." The highest praise given to paintings was "there is poetry in the painting." In spite of the difference in artistic form between poetry and painting, they both seek the same artistic conception: profound quiet; harmony with the orderly changes of nature. Thus the vivid charm of *qì* is the artist's positive agreement with and embellishment of the tranquility of both society and nature. This social tranquility and society's praise of the beauty of the tranquil found unity in painting. The living *qì* of the spirit resounds in profoundly quiet painting. This is the basic reason why the charm of *qì* occupies the position of primary importance in the theory of Chinese painting which emphasizes the expression of subjective intentions.

Méi Huā Tú (Plum Blossom) by Hong; early Qing Dynasty. In the collection of the Anhui Provincial Museum.

Not only does the *qì* function to connect the mind and spirit of the artist with the painting, it weaves the painter, the painting, and the viewer into a single unified experience. In fact, it stitches all of Chinese art into an elaborate, ongoing tapestry of continual creation, cultivation, and refinement of aesthetic imagination and imagery.

Yīn Jū Shí Lìu Guān (View from Secluded Dwelling), by Chen Hong Shou of the early Ming Dynasty. In the collection of the Taibei Imperial Palace Museum.

Section Five: Understanding *Qì*: Perception and Appreciation of Art

Traditional Chinese arts are so tightly woven together as to be inseparable. Indeed, many of the great poets of ancient China were also painters. Virtually all painters and poets were accomplished calligraphers. In his discussion of the artistic life of his country and his people, Lin Yu Tang explained:

> *The position of Chinese calligraphy in the history of the world's art is thus truly unique. Owing to the use in writing of the brush, which is more subtle and more responsive than the pen, calligraphy has been elevated to the true level of an art on a par with Chinese painting. The Chinese are fully aware of this when they regard painting and calligraphy as sister arts, shū-huà, "calligraphy and painting," forming almost an individual concept and always being mentioned in the same breath.*

He proceeds with a precise and vivid description of the relationship between these "sister arts" and the fundamental importance of the art of writing in Chinese painting:

It seems to me that calligraphy, as representing the purest principles of rhythm and composition, stands in relation to painting as pure mathematics stands in relation to engineering or astronomy. In appreciating Chinese calligraphy, the meaning is entirely forgotten, and the lines and forms are appreciated in and from themselves. In this cultivation and appreciation of the pure witchery of line and beauty in composition, therefore, the Chinese have an absolute freedom and entire devotion to pure form as such, as apart form content. A painting has to convey an object, but a well-written character conveys only its own beauty of line and structure.

Céng Dié Bīng Xiāo (Layers of Silk Taffeta), by Ma Lin; Southern Song Dynasty. Collection of the Beijing Imperial Palace Museum.

Owing to the inseparability of calligraphy and painting, it is only natural to find an equally intimate relationship between painting and poetry. The art of calligraphy developed naturally from the demands of the Chinese written character, and whereas calligraphy as an artistic form itself is indeed, as Lin Yu Tang observed, "pure form, apart from content," poetry in China, as in all other languages, has always been the art of enticing the deepest meanings out of words.

These deep meanings have always been inextricably bound with the philosophical ideals of the beauty and harmony of the natural world, that is, with the constant transformations of *qì*. The nature of "the Chinese written character as a medium for poetry" was brilliantly illuminated at the beginning of the 20th century by Ernest Fenollosa in an essay by that name. In it, Fenollosa remarks:

Chinese notation is something much more than arbitrary symbols. It is based upon a vivid shorthand picture of the operations of nature. ...

These embody true poetry as far as they go. Such actions are seen, but Chinese would be a poor language, and Chinese poetry but a narrow art, could they not go on to represent what is also unseen.

The best poetry deals not only with natural images but with lofty thoughts, spiritual suggestions and obscure relations. The greater part of natural truth is hidden in processes too minute for vision and in harmonies too large, in vibrations, cohesions and in affinities. The Chinese compass these also, and with great power and beauty.

You will ask, how could the Chinese have built up a great intellectual fabric from mere picture writing? To the ordinary Western mind, which believes that thought is concerned with logical categories and which rather condemns the faculty of direct imagination, this feat seems quite impossible. Yet the Chinese language with its peculiar materials has passed over from the seen to the unseen by exactly the same process which all ancient races employed. This process is metaphor, the use of material images to suggest immaterial relations.

In this Chinese shows its advantage. Its etymology is constantly visible. It retains the creative impulse and process, visible and at work. After thousands of years the lines of metaphoric advance are still shown, and in many cases actually retained in the meaning. Thus a word, instead of growing gradually poorer and poorer as with us, becomes richer and still richer from age to age, almost consciously luminous. Its uses in national philosophy and history, in biography and in poetry, throw about it a nimbus of meanings. These center about the graphic symbol.

The memory can hold them and use them. The very soil of Chinese life seems entangled in the roots of its speech. The manifold illustrations which crowd its annals of personal experience, the lines of tendency which converge upon a tragic climax, moral character as the very core of the principle—all these are flashed at once on the mind as reinforcing values with accumulations of meaning which a phonetic language can hardly hope to attain. Their ideographs are like blood-stained battle-flags to an old campaigner.

With us, the poet is the only one for whom the accumulated treasures of the race-words are real and active. Poetic language is always vibrant with fold on fold of overtones and with natural affinities, but in Chinese the visibility of the metaphor tends to raise this quality to its intensest power.

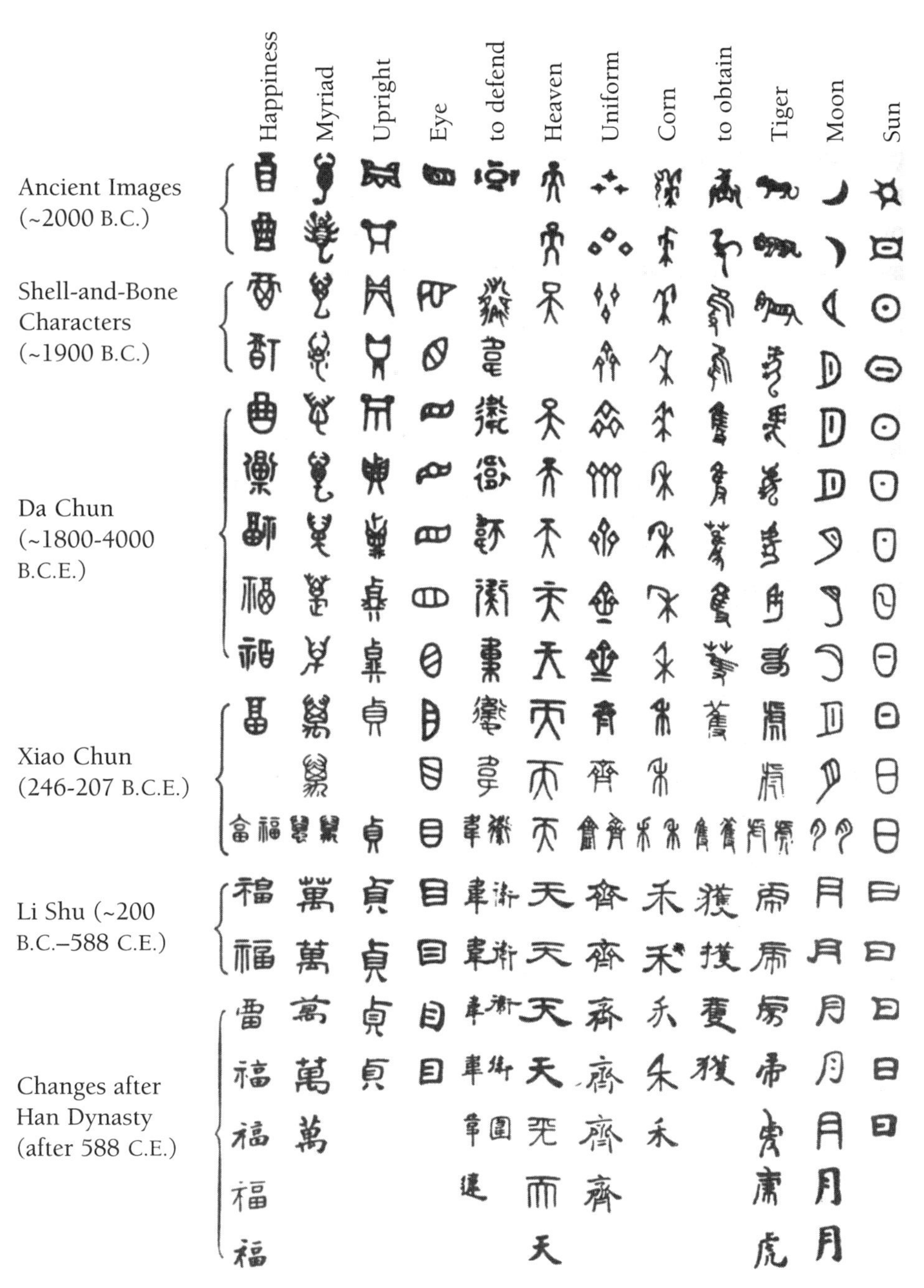

Table of historical changes of Chinese characters. From the book, *Chinese Calligraphy* by Chiang Yee (Harvard University Press, 1973).

What we have seen then is an organic interconnectivity throughout the entire field of view encompassed by all forms of art throughout Chinese history. Clearly and vividly, the concept of *qì* provides the woof and warp that binds this whole field together. What, then, is the position *qì* holds in the relationship between the artist, the work of art, and those who view, hear, or otherwise receive it? What do we need to know about the role of *qì* in art to correctly perceive, understand, and appreciate what traditional Chinese artists do and make in their art? Indeed, of what importance and benefit is an understanding of *qì* in the appreciation of works of art?

To find answers to such questions we looked into sources that span more than 2000 years of literary and artistic criticism in China. In the Three Kingdoms period (220 C.E.–265 C.E.), Prince Cao Pei of the Kingdom of Wei pointed clearly to the role of *qì* in the literary arts.

> *The principle of literature is qì. . . . It lays emphasis on the influence of the character of the writer's self in determining the style of the literary work. It reveals itself in the level of the writer's grasp of nature. It is the basic instinct of life itself.*

That *qì* serves as the motive force of painting is illustrated in the following story about the legendary "Saint of Painting," Wu Dao Zi, in the *Records of Famous Painting From Tang Dynasty* (*Táng Dài Míng Huà Jì*):

> *Wielding the paintbrush, he has the momentum of a whirlwind. Once General Pei Min gave gold and silk to Wu Dao Zi and asked him to paint a picture for him. He did not accept the general's gift. But he asked Pei Min to perform his sword form for him, so he might observe the qì of the general's strength to help him wield his paintbrush. After the performance of the sword, Wu Dao Zi took up the brush with force and vitality and completed the requested painting in a flash, as if an unseen spirit helped him from within.*

The General's riches could not commission a painting, but his *qì* literally impelled it through his sword, into the artist's mind, and out of the artist's brush. It is hard to conceive of a more intimate relationship between artist and audience. Thus we see that as in philosophy and medicine, *qì* is everywhere in Chinese art. In the Liang period of the Southern Dynasty (502 C.E.–557 C.E.), Zhong Rong wrote in his Preface to *Classes of Poetry* (*Shī Pǐn Xù*):

> *Qì changes nature. The changes of nature touch people. Thus qì arouses feelings and emotions. It manifests in dancing and recitation [of songs and poems].*

As long ago as the Spring and Autumn period (770 B.C.E.–476 B.C.E.), the importance of *qì* in the arts was recognized and memorialized. In the *Spring and Autumn Annals (Chūn Qiū)* it is recorded, "The will is fulfilled by *qì*. The choice of words is decided by the will."

Two thousand years later, Dong Fang Su, a writer in the Qing Dynasty (1644 C.E.–1911 C.E.), testified to the continuing survival of *qì* as the basis of artistic judgments:

In observing humans as well as all forms of animal and plant life, it can be seen that these all exist because of the arousal of qì. Once the qì is gone, only the unbearable stench of rottenness remains. One cannot tolerate being close to it. It is the same with poetry and literature.

Another Qing writer, Shen Zhong Qian, made the point even more directly:

All things are created through the receipt of the qì of heaven and earth. Thus each has its own spirit. Any attempt to draw a thing with brush and ink ought not only follow its shape but its spirit.

The implications now seem obvious. To perceive, understand, and appreciate Chinese art, we must comprehend the idea as well as the movement of *qì*. Just as artists rely on *qì* to power and guide their aesthetic principles and expressions, so must we be guided by *qì* to receive that which has been bestowed in such works of art. Only then can we fully connect with the spirit of the original. Only then can the vitality of the work enliven us.

In experiencing works of traditional Chinese art, we can not overlook the comprehensive importance of *qì*. Not only does the presence of *qì* in the artwork itself allow the viewer or reader to connect intimately with it, it can serve a curative function as well. This point is illustrated in a story from the Warring States period (475 B.C.E.–221 B.C.E.), told by Mei Cheng of the Western Han Dynasty (206 B.C.E.–25 C.E.) in a work entitled *The Seven Issues (Qī Fā)*. The story goes:

There was a young man, Prince Chu. He had been sick for a long time. His health was exhausted, for he had to remain in bed constantly. The illness had invaded so deeply that even herbal medicine and acupuncture could not help. One night however, Prince Chu received a guest from the state of Wu who told him stories of nature. He recounted these stories vividly, especially the ones about the hunt and about watching the waves at the oceanside. Suddenly, listening to his guest, Prince Chu felt the yáng qì become aroused. First it manifested between his eyebrows. At last it found its way continuously upward and outward until it filled up the entire house! As the night wore on, the guest from Wu continued his wonderful descriptions of the world in words, the mysteries and marvels, until his listener sat up in his bed. Without Prince Chu noticing it, his illness had disappeared.

Today the practice of healing arts is growing in popularity. By "healing arts" here we do not mean only the art of medicine. There is a growing movement in the mutual world of art and *qì gōng* that utilizes the presence of *qì* in all manner of artistic expression to heal patients suffering from a wide variety of diseases. Thus there are artist-healers who express their healing *qì* through their songs; others endow their paintings with their healing *qì* and hang them on the walls of their "patients'" rooms. There is growing recognition in the medical community that a patient's capacity to express his or her internal or mental imagery can exert a strong influence in that individual's healing process. To those steeped in the traditions of *qì* and the traditional arts of China, such phenomena are easily understood as manifestations of the mysterious and wonderful power of *qì*.

In the *Yellow Emperor's Classic of Internal Medicine,* the Emperor's physician, Qi Bo, points out that the shaman or *wū* treat their patients through "mobilizing the *jīng* (essence) and transforming it into *qì*." In such curious manifestations and phenomena the embrasive characteristic of *qì* expresses itself unmistakably as the great connective force of nature, the force that unifies all humankind, all the arts, all of creation. It was just this powerful connective force that found its most detailed expression in traditional Chinese medicine, which is where our journey through the history of *qì* next leads us.

Qì character. Calligraphy by Wang Mu Ji.

Anatomical painting by Huang Gu, 1684

Chapter 4

Qì in Medicine

The mere use of words is futile when you do not know what they stand for.

—Carl Jung

In China, when a doctor tells a patient that "the problem lies in the *qì*," that, as often as not, is the end of the story. But for those who approach Chinese medicine from afar, the story begins with *qì*. At least this is where the story ought to begin. For to understand anything that doctors of Chinese medicine are doing, we have to come to terms with what they mean when they use this well-worn word. The search for understanding is not always straightforward, and it is seldom easy. To search for the meaning of *qì* in Chinese medicine, we have to follow many paths. As we have suggested and pointed out in the foregoing chapters, these paths lead through the realms of music, painting, poetry, handwriting, philosophy, and a virtual forest of literary traditions. Now we find ourselves in the "great treasure house of traditional Chinese medicine"as Mao Ze Dong called it, and we shall trace the path of *qì* through this curious collection of artifacts of the Art of Benevolence.

To understand the meaning and function of the concept of *qì* in traditional Chinese medicine, it is important to grasp something of the nature of traditional medicine's long-term development as well as its relationship to other scientific, academic, and cultural disciplines in China. Medicine developed in China over a span of thousands of years. Its roots dig deep into prehistoric times when magicians spun webs of sympathetic magic into every aspect of peoples' lives. These ancient sorcerers, the *wū*, relied upon the fundamental forces of nature and their own unique abilities based in chants, dances, herbal concoctions and other forms of primitive, ritualistic medicine. They worked their magical medicine to intervene between unseen demons and the living who had been stricken by disease.

As civilization grew and developed in China, so did the art and science of medicine. By the second century B.C.E., the theories and practices of medicine had been refined, formalized, and recorded in one of the oldest and most comprehensive compendiums of medical science known, the *Yellow Emperor's Classic of Internal Medicine* (*Huáng Dì Nèi Jīng* 黃帝內經). In the following sections we quote extensively from the *Simple Questions* (*Sù Wèn* 素問) section of this medical classic. This book, which consists of two major sections, *Simple Questions* (*Sù Wèn* 素問) and the *Spiritual Pivot* (*Líng Shū* 靈樞), contains over 3000 references to *qì* in addition to the other fundamental substances of traditional human anatomy and physiology in ancient Chinese terms. From study of these ancient texts it is clear that among the primary concerns of medical practitioners in China for the past 2000 years, none has been more important than the patient's *qì*.

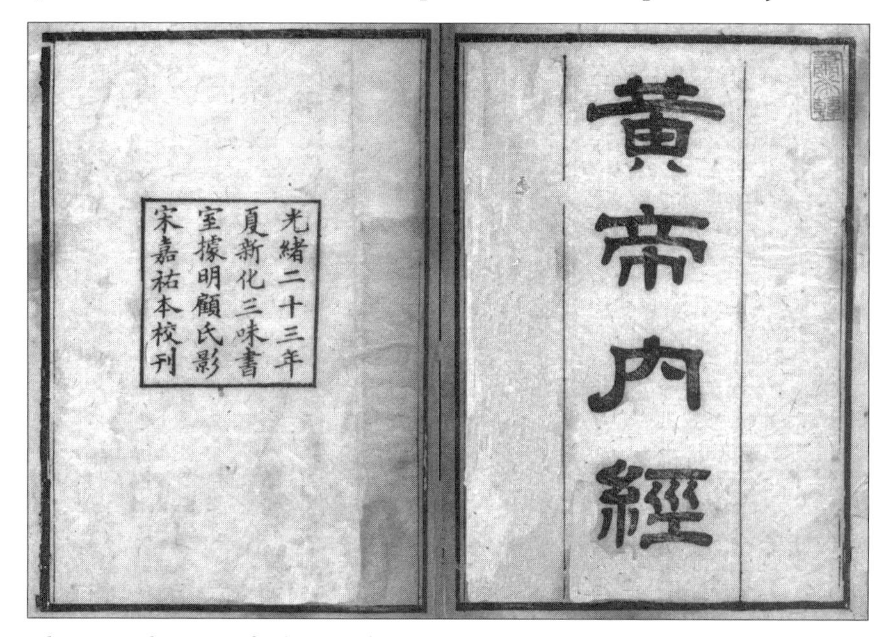
光緒二十三年夏新化三味書室據明顧氏影宋嘉祐本校刊

黃帝內經

Title page and reverse of title pages from Qing Dynasty copy of the *Nèi Jīng*, dated 1897.

Like the early proto-sciences of chemistry (alchemy), astronomy, and mathematics in ancient China, medicine developed according to elaborate philosophical theories such as those discussed in Chapter Two. Hence, it shares a fundamental, organic structure with these and other learned disciplines. This organic wholeness is an important feature of traditional arts and sciences in China. In medicine particularly, as in art, it derives largely from the concept of *qì*.

SECTION ONE: THE CONCEPT OF *QÌ* IN MEDICINE

It is likely that medical theorists borrowed the concept of *qì* from philosophers to explain the forces that animate and control the observable functions of the human body. Indeed, one of the chief differences between traditional Chinese medicine and modern medicine is the comprehensive system of philosophical constructs which served as the basis of medical theory in ancient China and have survived until the present as the functioning rationale for medical interventions.

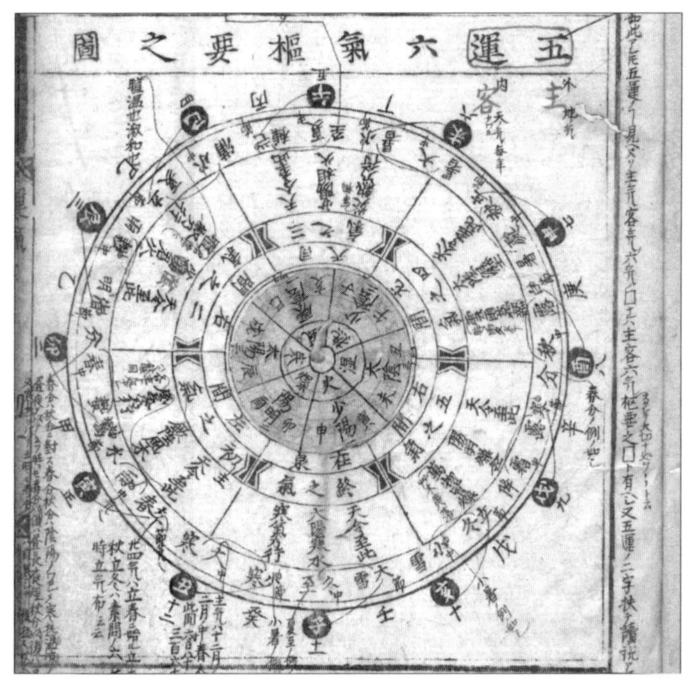

Pivotal Diagram of Five Movements Six *Qì* (*Wŭ Yùn Liù Qì Shū Yào Zhī Tú*) from the Song Dynasty text by Liu Weng Shu, *Sù Wèn Rù Shì Yùn Qì Lùn Ào*. The inner two circles are printed on a separate piece of paper that can be rotated allowing the user of this 1000 year-old "computer" to calculate the correspondence between various aspects of natural phenomena.

Among the most basic precepts of this philosophical approach to medical theory is the close relationship between humankind and our natural environment. Indeed, long before it was used as a term in medical treatises, *qì* appeared in cosmological treatises in which it was used to explain the origin and operations of the whole universe. The roots of such thinking can be directly traced to the native belief systems of ancient China which found eloquent expression in the works of Lao Zi, Zhuang Zi, and the Lao-Zhuang school of Daoist writers. Indeed, the human body was conceived as a microcosm of the universe. Thus it was natural for those who codified medical theories to apply the fundamental universal forces and substances to the task. If it is true, as we suggest, that the medical writers of ancient China borrowed *qì* from the philosophers, over the centuries they repaid the loan with substantial interest.

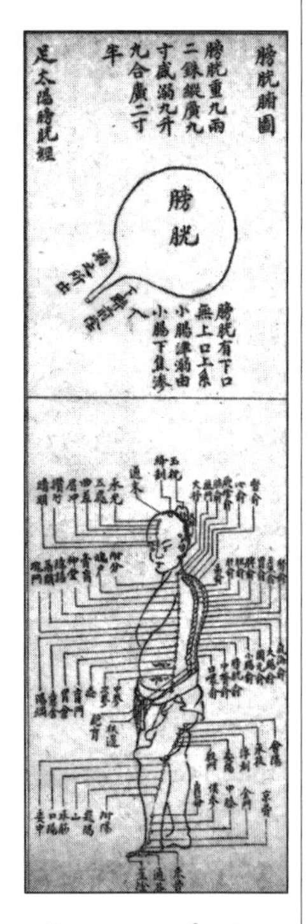

Páng guāng fǔ tú, a diagram of the urinary bladder and its associated channel pathway. From *Zhēn Jiǔ Dà Chéng* by Yang Ji Zhou of the Ming Dynasty.

Thus, *qì* became known as the vital substance of living beings. With the breadth and depth of the concept of *qì* to guide them, ancient theorists considered that just as it was seen to drive the winds through the atmosphere, accumulate in mountains and forests, and flow through rivers to the sea, *qì* must certainly circulate throughout the body itself. Thus a system evolved to account, in metaphoric terms, for the circulation of *qì*. This system served as the basis of the ancient anatomical and physiological model of human beings. This system was named *jīng luò* 經絡.

Contained within this name is one of the vital aspects of the *qì* in human physiology: connectivity. The word *jīng* 經 has several meanings including: warp (as in the warp and woof of fabric); longitude; manage, deal, or trade in; constant, regular; scripture, classic, or cannon; pass through, undergo; as a result of, through, or by way of; stand, bear, or endure. The idea of continuity or connectivity is present in all of these meanings. This sense develops from the pictographic elements that make up the character. On the left is the character *mì* 糹, which means "threads twisted together."On the right is the character *jīng* 巠, which means river, to flow, hence the course followed by a river. Threads that are twisted together along the main channels of flow in the body are known collectively as *jīng* 經. In Chinese medicine, the word *jīng* is used to name the main pathways through which *qì* and blood circulate to connect all parts of the body into a functional, organic unit.

This concept of interconnected wholeness is reinforced by the word *luò* 絡, which means "a net"or "anything resembling a net,"(i.e., anything having an interwoven structure). The *luò* comprise a finer level of circulatory pathways that branch from the *jīng* and serve to distribute the *qì* and blood throughout the body. These *luò* vessels also serve as the connectors between the *jīng* or main channel pathways.

This network of pathways through which the *qì* and blood circulate to every part of the body was well defined and illustrated more than 2000 years ago. It predates by more than 1500 years the "discovery"of the circulation of the blood by Harvey and its inclusion in Western medical theory. To the time of this writing, Western science has yet to acknowledge the presence in the body of the invisible movements the Chinese long ago recognized as the motive force causing and controlling the circulation of the blood and of life itself: *qì*.

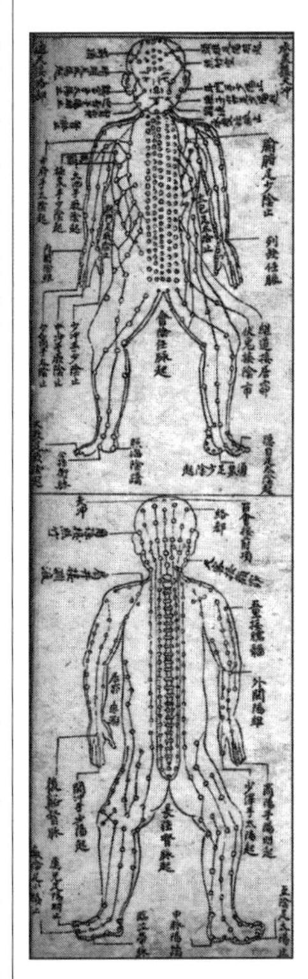

Jīng luò from *Zhēn Jiǔ Dà Chéng*, illustrating the connection points of the major channels.

Section Two: The Differentiation of *Qì* in Anatomy and Physiology

Ancient observers of the body in China became aware of the complex pattern of activities that constitute normal physiology. Thus, they were not content to accept a single, simple construct as the only explanation of all these diverse phenomena. They developed, therefore, a complex of varieties of *qì* each animating and controlling various aspects of human life: the opening and closing of pores, respiration and heartbeat, digestion and elimination, thought and emotion. The *Yellow Emperor's Classic of Internal Medicine* records over 270 different classifications of *qì*.

These divide into two categories, again, according to the philosophical roots from which Chinese medicine originally developed. These two categories are *yīn qì* and *yáng qì*. In studying these categories of *qì*, keep in mind that among the many properties and characteristics of *yīn yáng* theory, there is the notion that *yīn* always contains some *yáng* and vice-versa. Therefore, what follows is not a description of stark categorical differences. Rather, the differentiation of *yīn qì* and *yáng qì* follows a soft or fuzzy organization that emphasizes the primary tendencies of each variety of *qì* and takes into account that even the greatest *yīn* requires a germ of *yáng* to exist and function—and vice-versa.

The most *yīn* of the *yīn qì* is known as *yíng qì* 營氣 or *yīn yíng* 陰營. This is the nutritive substance that is derived from the food we eat by the digestive system and circulated throughout the body by the blood. The most *yáng* of the *yáng qì* is known as *wèi qì* 衛氣 or defensive *qì*. *Wèi qì* circulates outside of the *jīng luò* and serves as the outermost defensive mechanism of the body. These terms develop an extended metaphor that describes the body as an empire engaged in a struggle against disease. The word *yíng* means "camp," as in a military encampment. Here it embodies the sense of the body's substantive forces settled to nourish and prepare for this struggle through fortification of the body. The term *wèi* means "guard" as in a military sentry who stands vigilantly at the perimeter, defending the body against invasion.

Another of the *yáng* category of *qì* is the *yuán qì* 元氣 or original *qì*. This is the same phrase used to describe the state of *qì* (matter) before the inception of the universe, but the meaning in Chinese medicine is somewhat different. Like the primordial *qì* that filled Pan Gu's cosmic egg, *yuán qì* is understood as the most basic motive force of life within the human body. It is the force that emanates from the interplay of pure *yáng* and true *yīn*. It provides the primary impetus for growth and development of the body. It quickens every aspect of physiological function, all the organs, tissues, and cells. *Yuán qì* is the *qì* that provides the primary motive force for the circulation of both *qì* and blood through the pathways of the *jīng luò*. It drives yet another kind of *qì*, *jīng qì* 經氣 or channel *qì*, as it courses through the body. This *jīng qì* therefore falls into the *yīn* category as it is understood to be the complementary opposite of *yuán qì*.

Through the use of such conceptual tools, doctors of traditional Chinese medicine are able to perceive and analyze the functioning of the body in terms that are both precise and plastic. Thus they are able to isolate dysfunction to focus their diagnosis and adjust treatment accordingly. This is one example of the precision with which a well-trained doctor of Chinese medicine can understand what is happening in clinical situations.

In addition to such categories of *qì*, each of the internal organs is understood to have its own distinctive functional force or *qì*. Thus doctors of Chinese medicine speak of heart *qì*, lung *qì*, spleen *qì*, kidney *qì*, liver *qì*, and so forth. This system of classification correlates with the categorization of medicinal herbs and other substances so that a doctor can prescribe a medicinal formula designed to enter and affect a particular organ system or series of organ systems, depending on the constellation of symptoms that a patient presents.

The *qì* of each individual organ is also understood to govern a particular aspect of physiology. Thus, if there is a hearing dysfunction, a doctor is guided by such theories to the *qì* of the kidneys, which is traditionally said to manifest in the ears. Patients who present symptoms such as dream-disturbed sleep, irregular pulse, and a reddened tip of the tongue, among other typical symptoms, are carefully assessed for disturbances in the *qì* or function of the heart, as all of these are characteristics of disturbances of the heart *qì*.

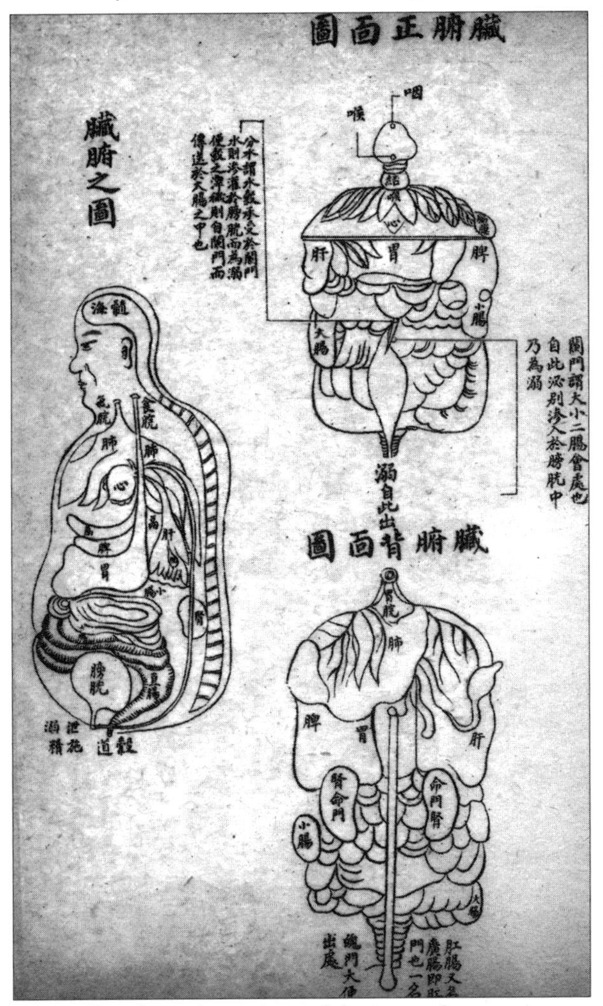

Zàng fǔ tú: three views of the internal organs: front, side and back (*op. cit*).

Problems in the general circulation of the *qì* as well as emotional problems, particularly a tendency to rage, are symptomatic of dysfunction of the *qì* of the liver. One of the normal functions of the liver *qì* is to control the patency of *qì* throughout the body. Severe disturbances of the liver, particularly organic damage—known in Chinese medicine as damage to the liver *yīn* or liver substance—can result in a condition known as "internal wind," "liver wind,"or "wind strike." One of the more commonly seen diseases in acupuncture clinics in hospitals of traditional Chinese medicine in the People's Republic of China is apoplexy and its sequelae. We have personally seen numerous cases of paralysis, both hemiplasias and quadriplasias resulting from stroke, successfully treated through the use of acupuncture and Chinese herbal medicines. Diagnostic theories such as the role of the *yīn* and *yáng* of the liver in the etiology of stroke enable doctors of Chinese medicine to address and effectively treat illnesses and ailments that their counterparts in hospitals purveying only Western medicine find difficult or impossible to treat.

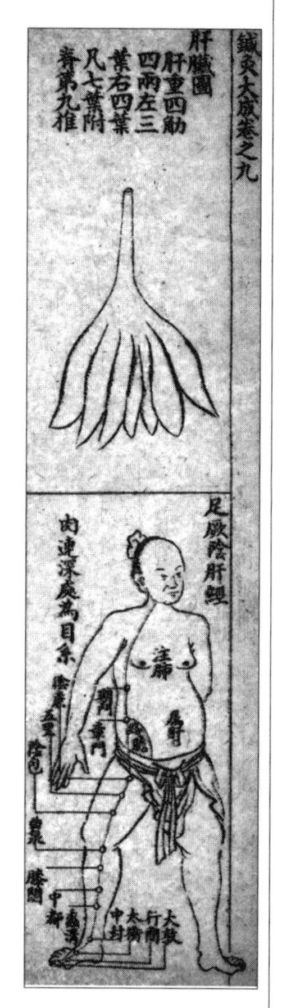

Gān Zàng Tú, showing the liver and its associated channel pathway. *Op. cit.*

Section Three: The Role of *Qì* in Diagnostics and Therapeutics

With respect to his or her patients, among the primary concerns of a doctor of Chinese medicine is the condition of the *qì*. Is the *qì* vacuous, that is, has its normal continuity become interrupted? Is the *qì* replete? Depleted? Does it flow freely? Or is the *qì* obstructed in a particular organ system or channel pathway?

The well-trained practitioner of Chinese medicine has extensive tools at his or her disposal to use in answering such questions. In the next section we list the main theoretical tools related to *qì*. Here, in general terms, are the roles that *qì* plays in the diagnosis and treatment of cases. It holds a central position in case management. The primary concern is an assessment of the patient's *qì*, for if its condition is understood and it can be effectively harmonized and brought into balance, the patient will begin to recover. We should also maintain the broader perspective afforded by the concept of *qì*. As we noted near the end of

Section Three in Chapter Two, Zhuang Zi said, "If the *qì* of *yīn* and *yáng* are not in harmony there will be disaster." Thus well-trained doctors of Chinese medicine act first and foremost to balance the *qì* and avoid disaster.

Since it is one of the primary symptoms that drive patients into the clinic, we begin with an examination of pain and its relationship with *qì*. To the doctor of Chinese medicine, pain can be divided into two major categories depending upon its main characteristic. A typical sequence of questions asked of patients in a traditional Chinese clinic is, "What type of pain do you experience?" "Is it fixed or does it move?" "Is it an achy pain or a stabbing pain?" "Is the pain alleviated or intensified by pressure, by warmth?"

There is, of course, a nearly infinite variety of pains that individuals experience and few symptoms are more subjective than pain. Yet with a basic understanding of the relationship between pain and *qì*, a doctor of Chinese medicine can focus on the pain-causing ailment. The first principle of diagnosing pain is that pain is understood as a manifestation of stagnation. That is to say, the phenomena of pain generally results when something that normally should move is prevented from this natural flow. What are these somethings? Basically, there are just two: *qì* and blood.

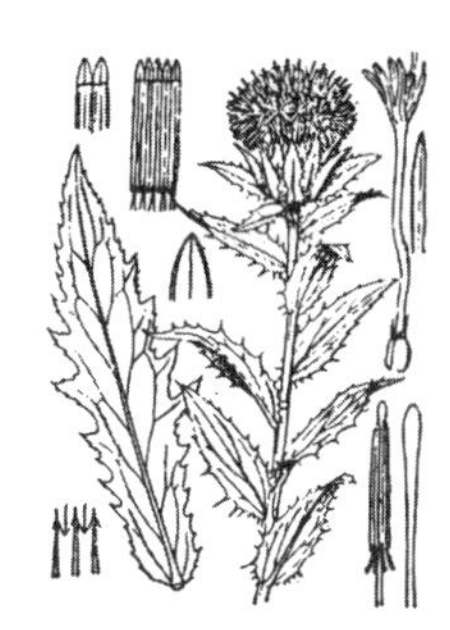

Hóng huā (red flower, *Carthami flos*)

Fixed, stabbing, and localized pains are classified as blood stagnation. A typical example is the pain that results from trauma. Moving, achy pains; pains that come and go; vague pains that are hard to pinpoint in location —all are indications of stagnation of *qì*. Such differentiation is of particular importance to doctors who treat with herbal medicines, for in the herbal pharmacopoeia there are specific medicinals that resolve blood stagnation as well as those that are used to restore the normal flow of *qì* when it has become obstructed or flows counter to its usual direction. Typical examples of each kind are the herbs known as *hóng huā* 紅花, literally "red flower" (*Carthami flos*), and *chén pí* 陳皮, tangerine peel (*Citri*

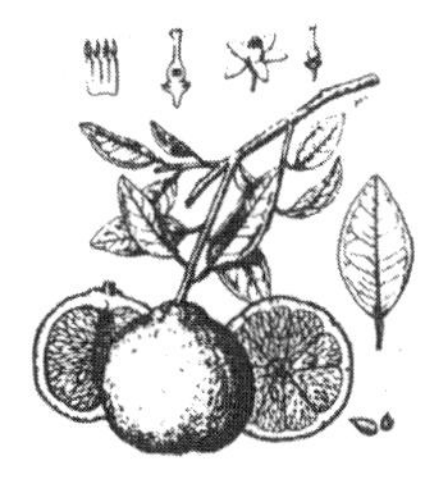

Chén pí (tangerine peel, *Citri exocarpium*)

exocarpium). Hóng huā is is famous for its ability to "move the blood" (i.e., to treat the pain that results from blood stagnation). Likewise, *chén pí* is often included in formulas designed to treat a variety of patterns that include pains arising from *qì* stagnation. It is remarkable that neither herb is particularly effective in treating pains of the opposite character. *Hóng huā* has little effect on the dull, achy pains caused by *qì* stagnation; *chén pí* is of little use in treating fixed, stabbing pains from blood stagnation.

For the purposes of the preceding example, we have vastly oversimplified the procedure for composing medicinal ingredients in a medicinal formula. The point, however, is that an important aspect of diagnosing and labeling pain is the determination of whether or not the patient suffers from an affliction of the blood or of the *qì*. In actual clinical situations one often sees cases where such symptoms are combined. Thus, diagnosis is far more complex and requires a thorough understanding of the entire array of diagnostic tools to be effective.

Diagnosticians using the tools of traditional Chinese medicine are likewise able to assess the condition of a diseased organ system by differentiating whether the problem is mainly from a disorder of the affected organ's substance or its *qì*. Such a differentiation can only be made through extensive information gathering. Again, we present an oversimplified example as illustration.

A patient presents with chest pains, dream-disturbed sleep, and shortness of breath. Any competent physician, whether of allopathic or traditional Chinese medicine, would suspect heart trouble and order an ECG. However, the traditional Chinese doctor would also undertake a careful examination of the patient's pulse. Finding an irregular pulse that, according to the classifications of pulse diagnosis was "skipping" (i.e., that had no identifiable pattern of irregularity), the doctor of Chinese medicine would suspect that the trouble with the heart was organic in nature. That is to say, an irregularly irregular pulse is a key diagnostic sign indicating organic heart disease.

A patient with a similar pattern of symptoms but whose pulse was not irregular or whose pulse had an irregular pattern which predictably repeated would likely be classified as suffering from a disturbance of the heart *qì* (i.e., as having primarily functional difficulties of the heart). Naturally, further diagnostic checks would be required to substantiate such a diagnosis. It is important to note that like their allopathic counterparts, doctors of Chinese medicine are not merely engaged in developing clever diagnostic pictures of their patients. They are searching for an entrance point to the case, that is, for a way to begin a therapy capable of ameliorating the patient's underlying problems.

The importance of being able to differentiate between those problems which are of a substantial or organic nature and those which reflect disturbances of an afflicted organ's *qì* is vital to the proper practice of traditional Chinese medicine. Within the diagnostic framework of Chinese medicine those of the former category are classified as *yīn* ailments; disturbances of the *qì* fall in the *yáng* category. A patient whose disease does not involve organic damage but is limited to disturbance of the *qì* of any given organ or system can be treated in an altogether different way than those whose organs have been damaged through injury or the advance of an organic disease process. This is of great significance to a large scale, institutional or, broader yet, a societal view of case management, particularly given today's stress on managed and capitated care. And, it bears repeating, none of this is intended to suggest that physicians can or should operate without recourse to any and all the advanced diagnostic procedures available to them.

Certainly competent doctors of traditional Chinese medicine will include such procedures whenever they are available. But it is extremely significant to note that without such modern techniques, well-trained physicians using only such ancient diagnostic tools have routinely and correctly diagnosed cases of both organic and functional disorders of the heart, liver, kidneys, lungs, and so on. The aim of many contemporary practitioners—and one very positive trend in today's leading medical institutions—is to combine traditional tools and techniques with advanced procedures whenever possible. Foremost among the traditional theoretical tools of Chinese medicine are those which enable a physician to understand how patients' symptoms have resulted from and affected their *qì*.

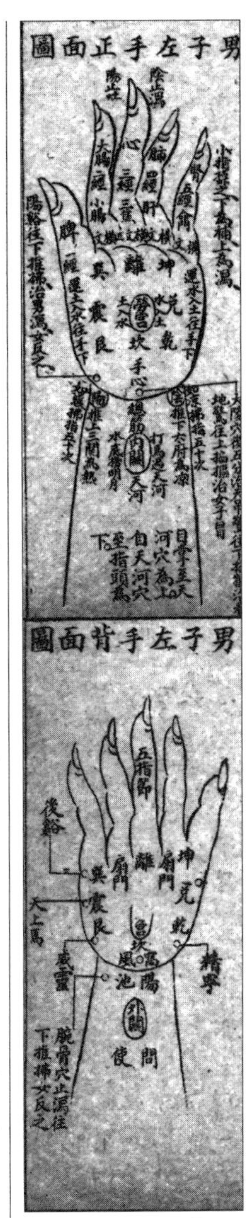

Nán zǐ zuǒ shǒu zhèng miàn tú and *nán zǐ zuǒ shǒu bèi miàn tú*. Front and back views of the left male hand, showing the positions of the relevant channels and associated trigrams. From *Zhēn Jiǔ Dà Chéng*.

It is a sad fact but one that it is urgent to acknowledge, that a very large number of surgeries performed each year in the United States are unnecessary. Perhaps, if medical doctors in the States were trained in the diagnostic tools of traditional Chinese medicine and thus able to identify those patients whose conditions could be successfully treated through low-intervention techniques designed to strengthen and rectify their *qì*, some if not many of such unnecessary procedures could be avoided. This is but one of the many benefits that could accrue from the integration of traditional Chinese medicine into contemporary health care delivery systems. It is a reason that motivated us to write this book, so that those who seek to understand the basic concepts of Chinese medicine can gain a foothold and establish a way to proceed.

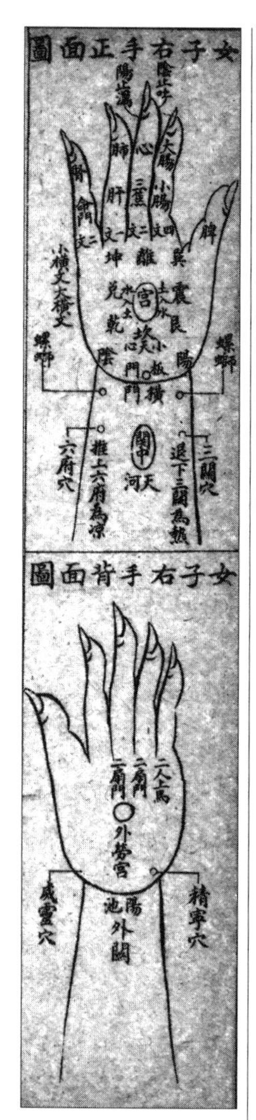

Nǚ zǐ yòu shǒu zhèng miàn tú and *nǚ zǐ yòu shǒu bèi miàn tú*. Front and back views of the right female hand, showing the positions of the relevant channels and associated trigrams *(op. cit.)*.

Section Four: Nourishing and Treating *Qì* for Health and Longevity

For more than 2000 years China has had many traditional methods of cultivating *qì*. We discuss several of these in the following two chapters. In this section we examine the importance of developing healthy *qì* from a medical perspective. We also explore the use of naturally-occurring drugs as well as other modalities of traditional Chinese medicine for the purpose of developing and cultivating health and longevity by means of nourishing *qì*. This is not to suggest that such medical traditions and practices are categorically different from those practices described in Chapters 5 and 6. Indeed, there is a high degree of interrelationship between *qì gōng*, *tài jí quán*, and the practice of traditional medicine in China. The discipline of herbology (internal medicine, *nèi kē*), for example, is a highly developed science in China requiring extensive study. Only after years of dedicated study and practice can a doctor of Chinese internal medicine effectively treat disorders of *qì* and help patients foster healthy *qì*. Thus we begin with an examination of the principles of Chinese internal medicine with respect to the nourishment of *qì*.

For many reasons, we in the West have been given an erroneous impression of the relative importance of acupuncture and herbal medicine in China. Perhaps it is our fascination with needles, perhaps it is just a chance of transmission that we perceive acupuncture as the main discipline of traditional Chinese medicine. In fact, the essence of Chinese medicine is contained in the disciplines of internal medicine and herbology. Acupuncture is a sub-specialty of Chinese medicine. It is unfortunately typical of the way Westerners often misjudge Chinese traditions that English-speakers have mistakenly elevated acupuncture to superior importance. There are many states that license acupuncture practice but fail to recognize or license Chinese traditional internal medicine. This is more or less equivalent to licensing physical therapy while ignoring conventional drug therapy. Would that not result in a somewhat distorted pattern of medical care?

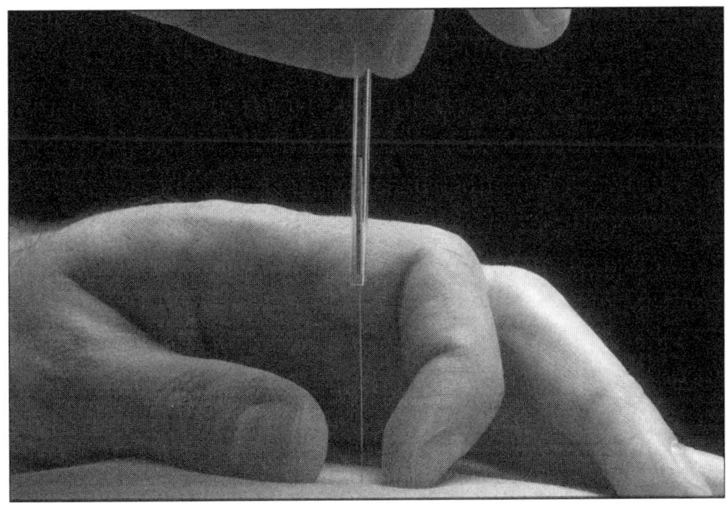

We mention this fact because in discussing the principles employed to influence the *qì* in Chinese herbology, we presume that readers will be rather less familiar with the subject than they are with the principles of acupuncture. A growing number of people in the West, doctors and lay alike, have come to accept the efficacy of acupuncture as a method of treatment. Far fewer recognize that the theoretical principles employed by acupuncturists are based on the principles of traditional Chinese internal medicine. This fact becomes particularly important in a discussion of how a doctor of Chinese medicine nourishes the *qì*, because acupuncture is not the modality of choice in cases where the *qì* is weak. One of our teachers, a veteran of the Chinese program launched in the late 1950s to establish modern schools of traditional medicine, emphasizes this point with a simple, rhetorical question: "How can you nourish anything with just a little steel needle?"

Another common Western misunderstanding concerns the nature of Chinese herbology itself. Chinese internal medicine makes use of many naturally-occurring drugs, some of which are herbs, some of which are animal or mineral products. Some are used essentially raw, others only after significant processing. Again, contrary to what the name "herbology" suggests, treatments are not the administration of herbal tisanes or teas as in Western traditional herbalism, but through theoretically justified formulas composed of, typically, two to twelve medicinals in proportions determined by a well-codified diagnostic process in which naturally occurring drugs are linked to specific symptoms and categories of disorder.

rén shēn (Ginseng radix)

One of the major classifications of Chinese medicinals is comprised of those that nourish the *qì*. One of the most famous of all the Chinese herbs belongs to this category: *rén shēn* 人參 *(Ginseng radix),* or as it is commonly known in America, ginseng. Others in this category include *huáng qí* 黃芪 (*Astragali radix,* astragalus root); *bái zhú* 白术 (*Atractylodis ovatae rhizoma,* atractylodes); *shān yào* 山藥 (*Dioscoreae rhizoma,* dioscorea); *biǎn dòu* 扁豆 (*Lablab semen,* lablab); *dà zǎo* 大棗 (*Ziziphi fructus,* jujube); *gān cǎo* 甘草 (*Glycyrrhizae radix,* licorice root); and *huáng jīng* 黃精 (*Polygonati huangjing rhizoma,* polygonum).

shēn

In the medical assessment and treatment of *qì*, it is often necessary to deal with a variety of conditions. Weakness or insufficiency of *qì* is seen often in the traditional clinic, but the *qì* can also be stagnant, not moving or stuck. This condition can arise to affect specific organs or parts of the body, or it can affect the entire organism.

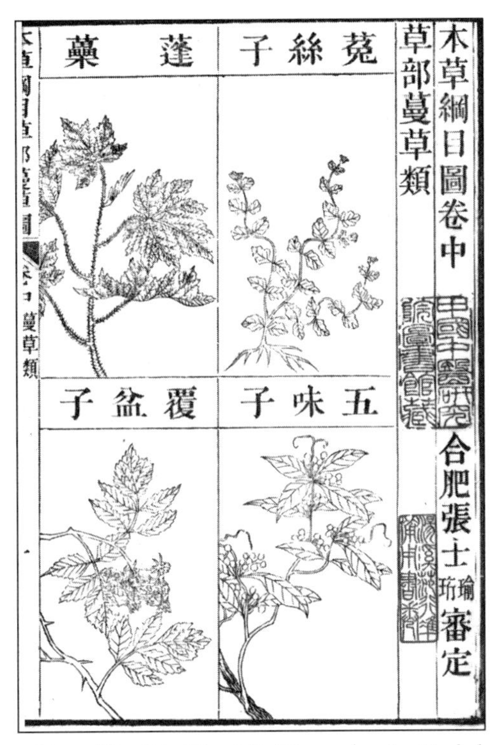

From *Běn Cǎo Gāng Mù (Comprehensive Herbal Foundation)* printed in 1885.

Another pathological condition of the *qì* occurs when it rises uncontrollably. This is typically from hyperactivity of the *qì* of the liver resulting from disease or injury to the liver *yīn* or blood. In such cases, doctors of traditional Chinese medicine turn to the category of herbs that calm or harmonize the *qì*. This category includes: *chén xiāng* 沉香 (*Aquilariae lignum*, aquillaria); *jiàng xiāng* 降香 (*Dalbergiae lignum*, dalbergia); *hòu pò* 厚樸 (*Magnoliae cortex*, magnolia bark); *bīn láng* 檳榔 (*Arecae semen*, areca); *dīng xiāng* 丁香 (*Caryophylli flos,* clove); and *shì dì* 柿蒂 (*Kaki calyx*, persimmon calyx).

Thus there is another frequently used category of Chinese medicinal herbs that are used to break bound *qì* and to mobilize *qì* that has stagnated. The herbs typical of this category include: *zhǐ shí* 枳實 (*Aurantii fructus immaturus,* unripe bitter orange); *chén pí* 陳皮 (*Citri exocarpium,* tangerine peel); *qīng pí* 青皮 (*Citri exocarpium immaturum*, green tangerine peel); *mù xiāng* 木香 (*Saussureae radix*, sassurea); *xiāng fù* 香附 (*Cyperi rhizoma,* cypress); *wū yào* 烏藥 (*Linderae radix,* lindera); *dà fù pí* 大腹皮 (*Arecae pericarpium,* areca); and *fó shǒu* 佛手 (*Citri sarcodactylidis*, Buddha's Hand).

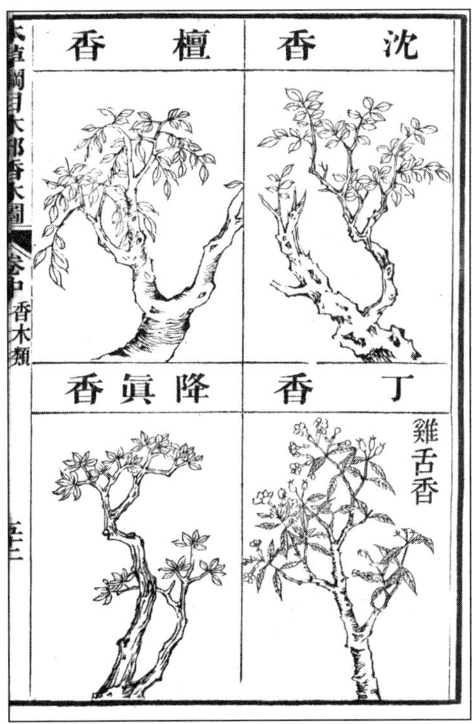

From *Běn Cǎo Gāng Mù (Comprehensive Herbal Foundation)* printed in 1885.

According to the basic principles of Chinese herbal medicine, these herbs are rarely used by themselves. Rather they are formulated into prescriptions that combine a number of different ingredients each having its own function. Herbs are carefully selected according to the patient's pattern and the rules of formula writing so that the combination will have the overall effect needed to improve the patient's condition. There are thousands of formulas that have been recorded over the centuries, and among these there are hundreds which are commonly used in clinics all over the world today.

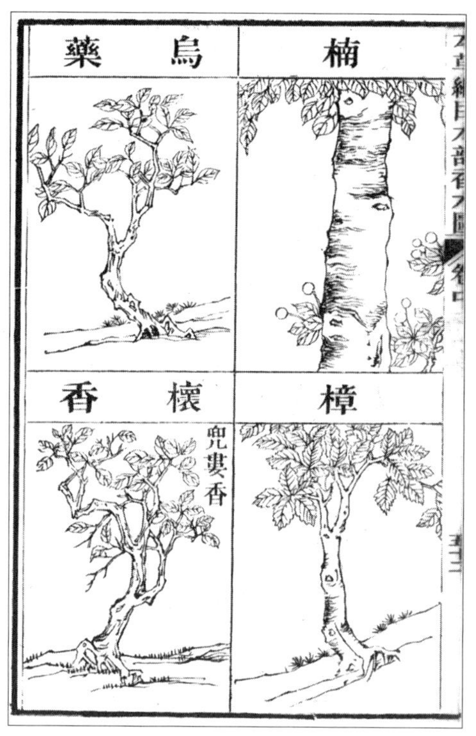

From *Běn Cǎo Gāng Mù (Comprehensive Herbal Foundation)* printed in 1885.

Typical formulas to nourish the *qì* include: *Sì Jūn Zǐ Tāng* 四君子湯 (Four Gentlemen Decoction), consisting of *rén shēn* 人參, *bái zhú* 白朮, *fú líng* 茯苓, and *zhì gān cǎo* 炙甘草; *Shēng Mài Yǐn* 生脈飲 (Pulse Engendering Drink), consisting of *rén shēn* 人參, *mài mén dōng* 麥門冬, and *wǔ wèi zǐ* 五味子; *Bǔ Zhōng Yì Qì Tāng* 補中益氣湯 (Center Supplementing *Qì* Boosting Decoction), consisting of *huáng qí* 黃芪, *zhì gān cǎo* 炙甘草, *rén shēn* 人參, *dāng guī* 當歸, *jú pí* 橘皮, *shēng má* 升麻, *chái hú* 柴胡, and *bái zhú* 白朮.

Whereas there is a high degree of similarity between the chemical components found in both herbal and modern pharmaceutical medicine, there are fundamental differences between the methods employed in Chinese medicine and those of modern allopathic medicine. These exist at virtually every step of the process, from theory through diagnosis and treatment. Western medical doctors seek to identify the disease-causing organism that has caused the diseased condition of the patient. They select drugs and medicines designed to destroy these pathogens and thereby cure the disease. The advent of gene therapies reflects a recent broadening of therapeutic strategy in modern biomedicine which, curiously, more closely approaches traditional Chinese thinking. Doctors of traditional Chinese medicine employ a system of theoretical principles that weave diagnosis and treatment into a continuous series of images that form a integrated view of the patient in the midst of the various environmental factors present in each individual case. In using Chinese medicines, the chief concern of a traditional Chinese medical doctor is how to employ the *qì* of the various ingredients to influence the patient's *qì*.

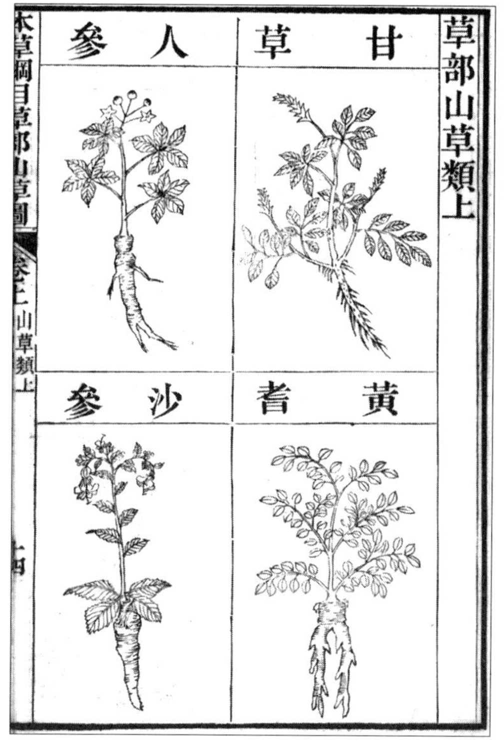

From *Běn Cǎo Gāng Mù (Comprehensive Herbal Foundation)* printed in 1885.

Thus Chinese herbs are categorized according to the nature of their *qì*. That is, there are categories of Chinese herbs that describe the *qì* or the functional effect shared by each herb in that particular category. Additionally, herbs are categorized according to their flavor, the organ and circulatory pathways they most readily affect, and other distinguishing characteristics as well.

With respect to the *qì* or basic nature of Chinese medicinals, there are four main categories: herbs that are cold in nature, herbs that are hot in nature, herbs that are warm in nature, and herbs that are cool in nature. Of flavors there are five: sour, bitter, sweet, pungent, and salty.

Every medicinal in the traditional Chinese pharmacopoeia has its own *qì* and flavor. These are of fundamental importance in the selection of herbs to treat different conditions. For instance, if the patient suffers from an invasion of heat and manifests symptoms that are characteristic of a hot pattern, this indicates to the doctor that the patient's *qì* is too hot (meaning that it shows the characteristics of being active, rising, and rapid) and can be treated with herbs that are cool and/or cold in thermonature to normalize the *qì*. A formula is thus designed to closely match each individual patient's condition, as the prescribing doctor selects each formula constituent according to the degree of their thermonature, the functional or physical area of the body each tends to affect, and the relative strength of effect that is appropriate for a particular patient.

This system is based entirely upon the philosophical roots we discussed in Chapter 2. That is to say, the concept and understanding of the *qì* of herbs developed directly from the philosophical concepts of the *qì* of heaven and earth, the interactive transformations of *yīn* and *yáng*. When we describe traditional Chinese medicine as comprehensive, it is this pervasive theoretical infrastructure which provides the basis of our description. Understanding the *qì* of the human body is similarly derived from these same theoretical principles. This is the rationale for using the *qì* of herbs to influence the *qì* of the human body: they are all manifestations of the same vast *qì* of nature and their ability to intervene in a disease process is the natural outcome of the universal function of their *qì*.

In Chinese medicine the pattern of interrelationships of the various aspects of this universal *qì* has been carefully mapped throughout thousands of years of theoretical and clinical development. Thus it possible to describe the precise systematic arrangement of the relationships between the *qì* of herbs, their flavors, and their medicinal functions. This system is based upon the concept of the *qì* of the five phases: metal, water, wood, fire, and earth. These five phases are correlated with the five principal *zàng* organs: lungs, kidneys, liver, heart, and spleen. This theoretical structure, though it may appear fixed and rigid, is remarkably fluid and adaptable in the hands of a well-trained doctor. It can be extended or expanded to include correlation of virtually any factor affecting a clinical situation. The emotions, environmental or exterior pathogens, and seasonal changes and influences can all be correlated through the application of this theoretical system.

To illustrate this, textbooks of Chinese medicine typically include charts and tables such as the one shown opposite. There are several important notes about such charts and tables. First, they are not intended to be quick-reference guides to clinical decision making. They merely illustrate the pattern of relationships that exist between various aspects and manifestations of *qì* in five-phase patterns. Second, it must be clearly and profoundly understood that every item in each aspect of the chart is itself a manifestation of *qì*. Those new to the subject of traditional Chinese medicine are prone to err by mistaking such formulations and illustrations as imperative categorizations demanding strict obedience in clinical practice. To the contrary, they are part of an eloquent theoretical method of illuminating the movements, transformations, and interconnections of *qì*. Such theories do not "determine" how well-trained doctors view or comprehend a patient's condition. They are not decision tables to be followed in rote observance. Rather, they provide conceptual tools that help a doctor understand what is happening with the patient's *qì*, how it has become disordered, and how it can be returned to the state of natural harmony that is health.

In the next section we examine some additional theoretical tools that doctors of traditional Chinese medicine employ to accomplish this in their clinical practices.

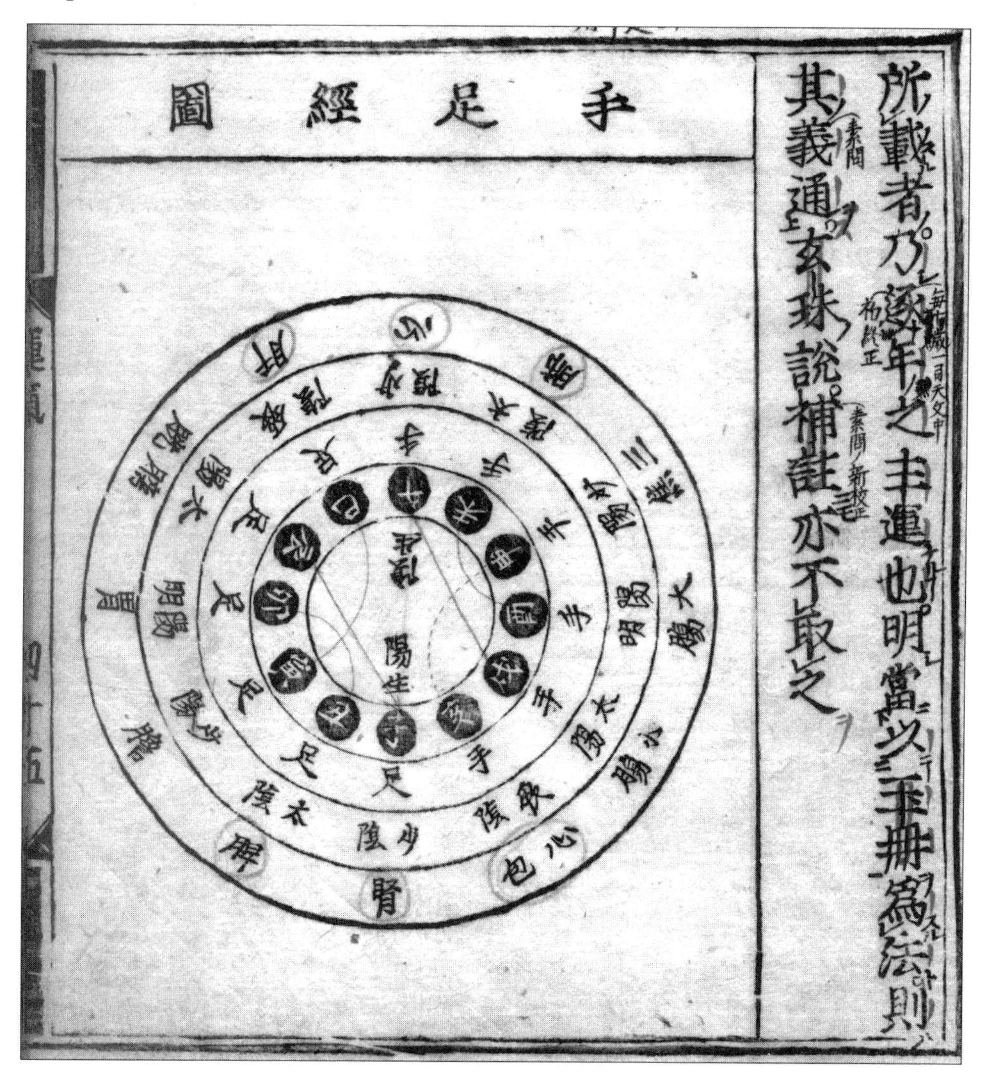

Channels of the hands and feet, showing correspondence of organs, channels, and earthly branches, and the cyclical *yīn yáng* relationships.
From the Song Dynasty text by Liu Weng Shu, *Sù Wèn Rù Shì Yùn Qì Lùn Ào.*

Section Five: Theoretical Tools to Identify, Analyze, Understand and Use the Movements and Influences of *Qì* in Traditional Chinese Medicine

The main feature of the theoretical tools available to a doctor of traditional Chinese medicine is their comprehensively coordinated interrelationships. The medium of this interconnectedness is *qì*. Not only does it interlace the structures and functions of the human body, it connects the body with the natural environment and the social and cultural structures in which humans actually exist. This results in a pervasive outlook on medical questions that can be considered as the primary theoretical tool. It is clearly illustrated in the following passage from the Song Dynasty Daoist classic by Zhang Jun Fang, *Seven Scrolls of the Cloud Classic* (*Yún Jí Qī Qiān*), Volume 35:

> *The physical body of human beings correlates to the situation of a country. The positions of the chest and abdomen are like the imperial palace and household. The distribution of the four limbs is like the countryside and borders. The various bones are like the hundred different classes of government officials. The shén is the monarch. Qì represents the people. If the people are controlled, the country is well managed. To stabilize and pacify the country, one must love the people. Thus, love the qì to achieve true health. The country will break down if the people are dispersed. A person dies if the qì is exhausted. The dead do not return to life. A broken country ceases to exist. Thus the sage vanquishes disaster before it comes to pass and treats illness before it invades. He gives medical care before anything has happened, not in the wake of disaster. The people are difficult to support and fall easily into danger. The qì is easy to adulterate and difficult to purify. Therefore, examine the virtue of power and prestige [in order to] to protect society. Disregard habits and desires [in order to] assimilate and stabilize the qì and blood. Thus can life be prolonged.*

A complex theoretical infrastructure grows from such roots. Here we present some of the essential features of this theoretical structure, that which has been characterized as "the vast treasure house of traditional Chinese medicine."[1]

[1]This is the famous quotation of Chairman Mao Ze Dong when he issued to call to arms that mobilized the Chinese medical community of the late 1950s to reestablish State-sponsored and supported institutions of traditional Chinese medical education and health care delivery for the first time in China for more than 100 years. Mao urged doctors to develop the "treasure house" of ancient Chinese medical traditions into a functional system that could be used to administer to the health care needs of the New China.

In determining the causes of disease, a doctor of Chinese medicine analyzes according to two basic categories of pathological conditions: internal and external. Among the external categories, we find the six replete *qì*. Under normal conditions, wind, heat, fire, moisture, dryness, and cold are all necessary phenomena that support life. They are meteorological factors which hold a close relationship with human physiology. In this normal state these six factors are known as the "six origins" or *liù yuán* 六元. But under various circumstances these climatic factors change beyond the limits of human tolerance and adaptation. Sometimes this is due purely to environmental phenomena; other times the same result obtains from a diminished capacity to adapt to environmental change. In either case, the result is illness. When illness results from such factors, the pathogenesis of the disease is classified as one or more of the six replete *qì*. Briefly, these are:

1. Wind. This is the main cause of disease in terms of traditional Chinese pathology. Wind has the capacity to arouse the other five pathogenic factors. If it arises in combination with cold, the resulting affliction is known as "wind-cold." If with intense heat, the condition is known as "wind-heat." Wind is recognized as "the cause of a hundred different illnesses."

Typically, wind first invades the outermost layer of the body, the skin. As noted earlier, the *qì* that functions at this level of the body is known as *wèi qì* 衛氣. If this *wèi qì* is strong and full, it is not easily affected by wind. If the *wèi qì* is weak, the body is easily invaded by wind. These phenomena correlate closely to the concept of "resistance" in terms of Western medicine. Injuries resulting from wind tend to afflict the upper portions of the body. In the *Simple Questions* section of the *Yellow Emperor's Classic* there is a passage to this effect: "Injured by the wind evil, the upper portion receives the influence first." Included in the meaning of "upper" are the lungs, which occupy the "upper *jiāo*."[2]

In normal physiology, the lungs control and manage the *qì*. The lungs, if unobstructed, distribute the *qì* throughout the body. When they are obstructed by wind, coughing results, along with other symptoms typical of what Western doctors call "upper respiratory disease."

2. Cold. Cold is the prototypical *yīn* pathogen. It injures the *yáng qì* of the body more readily than any of the other six replete *qì*. The *yáng qì* provides

[2] The *sān jiāo* (triple burner) comprises a "virtual" internal organ in traditional Chinese physiology. For a complete description of the *sān jiāo*, see *Practical Dictionary of Chinese Medicine*.

the energy that powers the internal organs. The *yáng qì* is controlled by the heart. Its root is in the kidneys. It originates in the spleen.[3] Thus, injuries caused by cold mainly affect the heart, kidney, and spleen *yáng*. The character of cold is to congeal and stagnate. Hence, injuries resulting from cold are characterized by stagnation of *qì*. In the *Simple Questions* section of the *Yellow Emperor's Classic of Internal Medicine* it states, "Cold causes the skin[4] to shut. Then *qì* cannot move through and stagnates."

Also, "Pain results from too much cold *qì*. If there is cold, there will be pain." For example, if the *yáng qì* of the heart is injured by cold, there will be pain in the chest and the fingers will be cold. If the spleen *yáng* is injured by cold, the pain will be in the abdomen; and there will be diarrhea with liquid stools containing undigested food. If the kidney *yáng* is thus injured, the pain will appear in the lower back; and impotence will result along with swelling due to an accumulation of excess body fluids. These are all typical symptoms of injuries from cold. The widespread nature of injuries arising from cold prompted one of China's greatest doctors of the Eastern Han Dynasty (25 C.E.–220 C.E.), Zhang Zhong Jing, to author a book which remains to this day among the most studied medical texts in the world, *On Cold Damage* (*Shāng Hán Lùn*).

3. Summerheat. This pathogenic factor has the distinct seasonal character of its name. Its essential nature is heat but it usually combines with dampness and easily injures the *yīn qì*. According to *Simple Questions* (*Sù Wèn* 素問):

> *When heat opens the skin[4], the thoroughfare of yíng 營 and wèi 衛 [i.e., the two complimentary aspects of the body's qì], the sweat is freely released. Thus, the qì escapes as well.*

In Chinese medicine, sweat is the fluid of the heart. Accordingly, the *qì* of the heart can be exhausted due to excessive sweating. Thus, heart *qì* is prone to injury by summerheat. Additionally, because the lungs control the

[3]The spleen, in Chinese medicine, is not equivalent to the Western concept of spleen. In Chinese medicine, the spleen is the main organ system of digestion and is linked in an interior-exterior relationship with the stomach. Together, these two organs are responsible for generating the *qì* of the whole body. The *qì* that originates in the spleen through the processes of digestion and metabolism is circulated to the lungs where it is blended with the *qì* extracted by the lungs from the air. In order to complete the "substance" of the *qì* which the body requires for healthy functioning, it then circulates to the kidney system where it is "rooted" i.e., blended with the essence or *jīng* 精 that is stored in the kidney.

[4]Here, the word "skin" refers to not only the outer integument of the body but the underlying strata as well, including the superficial layers of the skeletal muscles and, importantly, the pores, sweat glands, and sebaceous glands.

skin and the opening and closing of the pores, they thereby have the function of controlling and responding to the body's changes of temperature. This function depends upon the *wèi qì*. Conversely, the *wèi qì* depends upon the lung's primary function of dispersing the *qì* throughout the body. Of particular importance is the circulatory pathway of the *qì* from the lung to the kidneys where it is endowed with the vital essence stored in the kidneys. Therefore, when summerheat injures the *wèi qì,* the pores open uncontrollably. Excessive sweating results in loss of lung *qì*. Unchecked, this will also lead to loss of kidney *qì*. Thus, the symptoms typical of summerheat invasion are tiredness (that is, a shortage of *qì*), weariness, a flustered feeling, and aversion to wind. Serious cases include a weakening of the pulse from diminution of the *qì* of the heart, along with a weak and low voice. These symptoms all result from and reflect the injury of the heart, lung, and kidney *qì* from summerheat.

4. Damp. Dampness is the *qì* of "long summer."[5] Its nature is heaviness characterized by retention of body fluids. It readily injures the *yáng qì* and disturbs the normal functioning of the spleen, which is prone to damage by dampness. This injury is categorized as a "disturbance of the *yáng qì* of the spleen from dampness"or an "accumulation of dampness from spleen *qì* vacuity" The main function of the spleen is to transform and transport the essence obtained from food through the processes of digestion and metabolism. As mentioned earlier, the *qì* thus transformed from food by the spleen is circulated upwards to the lungs where it mixes with the atmospheric *qì* inhaled into the lung and separated by the lung for this purpose. When damp invades the body, this compromises the spleen's ability to send the pure *qì* extracted from the essence of ingested foodstuff. The *qì* of the "middle *jiāo*" (the spleen and stomach) then becomes stagnant and sinks instead of rising. Thus, the spleen is said to be intolerant of damp and easily injured thereby.

5. Dryness. The external pathogenic factor known as dryness is the replete *qì* of Autumn. In the early Fall, the temperature is still warm, but the humidity of summer has past. Then, dryness is accompanied by warmth. In the latter part of the season, the temperature drops and a cool dry climate arrives. Regardless of temperature, dryness readily attacks the lungs. The lungs are known as the "delicate viscus." That is to say that they are easily injured by external pathogens, particularly by dryness which robs necessary

[5] "Long summer" is a term that applies to the order of the four seasons. In some systems of reckoning the divisions of the year, an additional, fifth season, named "long summer," was interposed between Summer and Autumn.

moisture from the many mucosal surfaces of the lungs. When the lung is healthy and clear, the *qì* separated from inspired air moves freely downward. The typical symptoms of an attack of dryness are therefore cough (particularly non-productive cough with its absence of moisture), asthma, and an feeling of oppression in the chest.

6. Fire. The nature of fire is essentially the same as heat. In clinical practice these two are often mentioned together or interchangeably. Heat is a gradient of fire; fire is the extreme of heat. Clinically, the difference between heat and fire is used to analyze the progress and severity of disease. Both belong to the *yáng* category and thus can attack and destroy the *yīn* substances of the body. This can result in disturbances of the blood. The internal balance of *yīn* and *yáng* is then disturbed. One typical result of such disturbance is known as "internal wind." This commonly results when the *yīn* and/or blood of the liver is damaged. The liver governs the free flowing of *qì*; thus this pattern can result in dispersal of *qì*. As a result the *qì* fails to flow properly or in the proper channels and organs. Thus, fire can attack virtually every internal organ.

In addition to these six replete (environmental) *qì*, traditional Chinese medicine recognizes internal pathogenic factors. Chief among these are the seven affects, *qī qíng* 七情. These seven affects are: joy, anger, anxiety (worry), thought, sorrow, fear, and fright. Naturally thoughts and emotions occur frequently, and in normal, balanced circumstances there is nothing pathogenic about these experiences. The concept of endogenous pathogenesis resulting from these emotions relates to imbalance. Of particular importance in this concept of pathogenesis are both sudden emotional disturbances as well as long-term unabated emotional states. Not only are such disturbances known to result in mental dysfunction, they contribute to, or cause disease themselves, by disturbing the function of the internal organs and particularly the movement of *qì* throughout the body.

Each affect is correlated with one of the internal organs according to the following scheme:

Excess of anger disturbs the liver.
Excess of thought disturbs the spleen.
Excess of fear and fright disturb the kidneys.
Excess of joy injures the heart.
Excess of sorrow injures the lungs.

However, the most obvious disturbances resulting from emotional imbalances are disturbances of the *qì*. *Simple Questions* (*Sù Wèn* 素問) states:

I know that a hundred different diseases are generated by [disturbances of] qì. Anger causes the qì to rise. Excessive joy causes the qì to wallow. Excess of sorrow consumes the qì. Sudden fear causes the qì to collapse. Cold restrains the qì. Heat causes the qì to run recklessly. Fright disturbs the qì. Being overtired exhausts the qì. Anxiety depresses the qì.

One of the aspects of traditional Chinese medicine that makes it attractive to contemporary patients is the inclusion of emotional or psychological factors among the various disease-causing agents that a doctor of Chinese medicine considers in his or her patients. Modern people are beset with enormous strains and stresses of living fast-paced lives in times when traditional life styles have been greatly altered by the advent of new technologies. Contemporary civilization presents non-stop emotional challenges. In the ancient wisdom of Chinese medicine there are, perhaps, methods for comprehending the damage that modern life inflicts and for developing strategies to overcome these challenges, restoring the whole person to a state of radiant health.

Ancient Chinese medical theorists recognized that to enjoy a state of radiantly good health, a person must have proper nutrition, exercise, and lifestyle. Thus, in addition to external and internal pathogenic factors, traditional Chinese medicine also includes, among disease-causing factors, improper eating, failure to maintain adequate exercise, and various other problems resulting from the manner of conduct in daily life.

In traditional Chinese medicine, food is the source of two essential ingredients for life. One is essence or *jīng* 精, the other is *qì* 氣. As described above, the spleen is the organ for extracting and transforming these essential ingredients from the food we eat and transporting them throughout the body. Thus the spleen and stomach are highly susceptible to influence from food-induced illness. But in Chinese medicine food is understood to have a profound influence on each of the internal organs. This influence follows a pattern that corresponds with the theory of the five phases and is reflected in several similar schemes that relate not just food but color, sound, and as well the six *qì* and the seven affects, described above, with the five basic internal organs.

TABLE OF FIVE-PHASE CORRESPONDENCES

	WOOD	FIRE	EARTH	METAL	WATER
VISCUS	liver	heart	spleen	lung	kidney
BOWEL	gallbladder	small intestine	stomach	large intestine	bladder
SENSE ORGAN	eyes	tongue	lips	nose	ears
VISCUS STORES	blood	shen (spirit)	nutritive qi (chyle)	qi	jing (sexual essence)
TISSUE	tendons	vasculature	muscles	skin	bones
QUALITY	color	odor	flavor	tone	fluid
EXPRESSION	shout	laugh	sing	weep	groan
INDICATOR	nails	complexion	lips	breath	hair
SEASON	spring	summer	midseasons	autumn	winter
DIRECTION	east	south	center	west	north
COLOR	bluegreen	red	yellow	white	black
ODOR	rancid	scorched	fragrant	fishy	putrid
FLAVOR	sour	bitter	sweet	spicy	salty
EMOTION	anger	frivolity	worry/obsession	grief	fear/fright
ADVERSE CLIMATE	wing	heat	humidity	dryness	cold
STRESS RESPONSE	clenching	depression	hiccough	cough	trembling

In the case of food, this pattern is arranged according to idea of flavor. This is an extremely important aspect of Chinese medical theory, for it relates not just food but also medicinal herbs to the internal organic structures and functions of the human body. In fact, food and herbs occupy a continuum where they are distinguished by the relative danger of their use. Food can be likened to herbs of the highest value in that they are safe to use over time and in a broad variety of conditions.

The pattern of the interaction of the five flavors with the five internal organs is:

Bitter affects the heart.
Sour affects the liver.
Sweet affects the spleen.
Pungence affects the lung.
Saltiness affects the kidney.

In terms of nourishment, the preceding pattern suggests that each of the five internal organs can be nourished through eating foods and/or herbs with flavors that correspond accordingly. In terms of pathogenesis, a dietary imbalance of any of these flavors renders the corresponding organs susceptible to injury from flavors taken in surplus or deficit, that is, out of balance. A surplus of bitterness in the diet injures the heart; too much salty food can damage the kidneys; and eating too many sweets can impair the function of the spleen.

The entire basis for these dietary interactions is *qì*. It is the medium of these corresponding influences. Clearly, it is not the salty flavor itself which circulates from the stomach to the kidneys to create or mediate the influence observed. It is the way in which the entire organism responds to saltiness. In other words, what damages the kidney is the effect on the whole of organic function that follows eating too much salty food. Organic function is monitored by *qì*.

This pattern of influences derives from thousands of years of experience and clinical observations. It is arranged according to theories based upon the fundamental philosophical constructs of *yīn* and *yáng* and the five phases. These theories, as discussed in Chapter 2, are essentially elaborations on the nature and function of the *qì* of heaven and earth.

In human experience, this *qì* of heaven and earth constitutes the human organism and is also influenced by our behavior. Our daily habits, be they constructive or destructive, have a profound effect upon our *qì*. *Simple Questions* (*Sù Wèn* 素問) notes, "Too much strain exhausts the *qì*." But it also mentions that "too much lying in bed injures the *qì*." We discuss the role of movement and exercise in some detail in the following two chapters.

Another important aspect of human behavior that profoundly influences the *qì* is sexual conduct. This is a vast subject and was well-developed as a discipline of study and practice in ancient China. Doctors of Chinese medicine have understood the importance of sexual life in the welfare of their patients for thousands of years. A medical book entitled *Incisive Light on the Source of Miscellaneous Diseases (Zá Bìng Yuán Liú Xī Zhú),* written in the Qing Dynasty (1644 C.E–1911 C.E.), records the following:

> *According to the words of doctors, qì is the ancestor of shén [spirit]; jīng [essence] is the son of qì. Thus qì is the root of jīng and shén . . . If the jīng is injured the qì will be exhausted. When the qì is exhausted, the shén will disperse.*

One of the primary ways in which the *jīng* is injured is through over-indulgence in sexual activity. The word *jīng* 精 has several meanings. One of these is "essence,"as previously discussed; another is "semen." In studying ancient texts that deal with the subject of sexuality, it is often unclear whether the intended meaning of a particular use of *jīng* is, therefore, essence or semen. As we described in greater detail in our previous book, *Who Can Ride the Dragon,* it is a curious aspect of the Chinese language, particularly of the ancient form (which is the language of the medical classics), that words frequently mean several things at once. Thus, a confounding cloud often surrounds these ancient Chinese texts. One thing is clear, however: excessive emission of semen was understood by a consensus of ancient theorists to result in a depletion of *jīng* and thus a loss of *qì* and spirit. With typical balance these ancient materials also contain admonitions against refraining altogether from sexual activity lest the *jīng* stagnate and the (male) sexual organ become "like a snake turned to stone."

Balance in sexual life is considered of primary importance in the maintenance of health and wellbeing. It is noteworthy that the great preponderance of extant ancient materials on the subject of sexual practices almost entirely focuses on male sexuality. This is a reflection of the male-dominance of Chinese civilization throughout much of the Imperial era during which such books have been collected and passed from one generation to another. There do exist discussions, particularly in some of the works of Daoist sexual magic and alchemy, concerning the importance of female sexuality. These should be studied at greater length to ascertain a more comprehensive picture of ancient Chinese attitudes and beliefs.[6]

The understanding of *qì* in illness and health can be more deeply comprehended in terms of a further series of theoretical tools employed by doctors of traditional Chinese medicine. Beyond the simple identification of evils as originating in the exterior environment or the interior of the body, there are several means by which to analyze and understand the condition of a patient's *qì* in any clinical situation.

The most common of these analytical tools or observable scenarios is known as *qì xū* 氣虛 or "*qì* vacuity." According to *Simple Questions,* this condition affects the organism generally and is characterized by a discontinuity of *qì*. That is to say the fundamental function of the *qì* in connecting the organism into an integrated, functional whole is insufficient. Therefore, the whole system is in functional decline. Because, however, the generation of *qì* in the body is most closely related with the lungs, spleen, and kidneys, the manifestations of *qì* vacuity are more pronounced in the structures and functions that are related to these organs.

6 The subject of Chinese sexology and its relationship to the ancient practices of preserving health and attaining longevity is discussed at length in our forthcoming book, *One Square Inch.*

According to *Simple Questions* (*Sù Wèn* 素問), the lungs are in charge of the *qì* and perform the function of respiration. *Simple Questions* contains several comments regarding this insufficiency of *qì* in relationship to the lungs, including: "All the *qì* corresponds with the lungs"; and "*qì* vacuity is lung vacuity."

There are two meanings of the phrase, "the lungs are in charge of the *qì*." First, the lungs are the organs of breathing. Second, the lungs manage the diffusion of *qì* throughout the entire body. The breathing function depends upon the normal functioning of the lungs. The pathways for air remain unobstructed and the process of extracting *qì* from inspired air continues so long as the lungs function normally. This normal functioning of the lungs also regulates and adjusts the circulation of *qì* throughout the entire organism according to the following pattern. The *qì* extracted by the lungs from the air is blended in the lungs with the clear *qì* that ascends from the spleen, which has been extracted from food and water.

The lung and its associated channel pathway, from *Zhēn Jiǔ Dà Chéng*.

Furthermore, the lungs control the skin as well as the pores, hair follicles, and skin hair. Thus when the lungs are healthy and function normally, the skin will be lustrous and well-irrigated, and the hair on the skin will appear normal and healthy. When the lung functions are compromised and the *qì* becomes vacuous, the skin and hair appear dry and lacking in luster. This external layer of the body is closely related to the *wèi qì* (the defensive *qì* mentioned earlier) which is the body's outermost defensive mechanism. Thus patients suffering from *qì* vacuity are prone to invasion of various external evils. In other words, their resistance is weakened and they become less and less resistant to disease.

The most certain way to prevent this pattern of pathology from developing is to maintain the *qì* and ensure its normal, healthy circulation throughout the body. This can be done through a variety of means including proper exercise and diet, consuming herbal formulas specially designed to address and correct an individual's specific weaknesses, special breathing practices known as *qì gōng*, and practicing special methods of accumulating and cultivating *qì* such as *tài jí quán*. Here again, we see that the presence of *qì* in traditional Chinese medicine serves as a connective factor that provides a unique, holistic approach to the management of the fundamental factors underlying disease and, more importantly, good health. When properly understood and practiced, this approach can assist individuals to reach the ancient goal of the superior doctor: treating patients before they become ill.

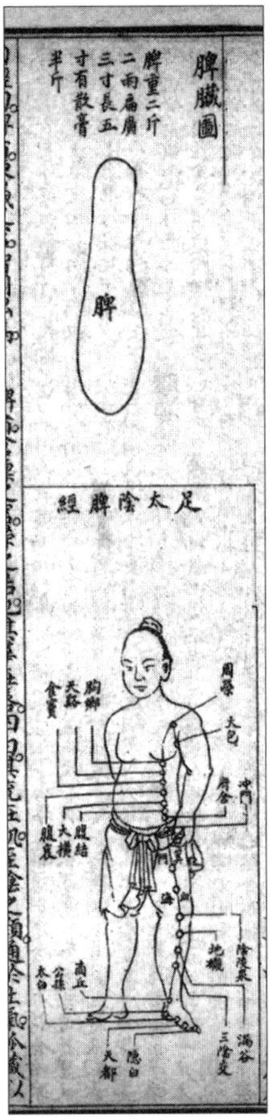

As we mentioned above, *qì* vacuity relates not only to the lungs but also to the spleen and kidneys. The spleen is the source of nutrients for growth and development. It is the organic system that acquires, transforms, and transports the essence of food to the entire organism. If the *qì* of the spleen is weak, the functions of digestion (i.e., transformation and transportation) are weakened. Such conditions are accompanied by the symptoms of lack of appetite, abdominal distention, exhaustion, and a frail constitution.

The spleen also promotes water metabolism. A weakened spleen is less able to transport fluids, resulting in fluid retention, edema, and accumulations of phlegm. This affects the *qì* that normally rises from the spleen to the lungs. The lungs then produce phlegm rather than clear, pure *qì*. Thus, another symptom typical of spleen *qì* vacuity is cough accompanied by phlegm, which can be copious at times.

The spleen and its associated channel pathway, from *Zhēn Jiū Dà Chéng*.

Furthermore, the spleen has the function of generating blood and maintaining the flow of blood within the vessels. Patterns characterized by spleen *qì* vacuity can include a variety of conditions in which blood flow is not properly contained within the blood vessels. Symptoms such as vomiting blood, hematuria, hemoptysis, metrorrhagia, and hemostasis are Western-named examples. The spleen functions in normal physiology to nourish and maintain the flesh. Conditions affecting the *qì* of the spleen therefore are frequently accompanied by symptoms such as flaccid muscles and pale complexion.

Finally, we read in such medical classics as the *Review of Medicine* (*Yī Shù*), written in 1826 during the latter part of the Qing Dynasty, that the kidney is the "root of *qì*," and "The kidney is the basis of original *qì*. It is the root of life. It must be nourished and preserved." The kidneys are considered the storehouse of original *qì* and of the prenatal essence. This essence or *jīng*, received from one's parents during the act of procreation, contains the fundamental blueprint of an individual's *yīn* and *yáng*. When the *jīng qì* of the kidneys is full and flourishing, *yīn* and *yáng* can function normally and harmoniously. Since the interplay of *yīn* and *yáng* is the basis of all life, this means that healthy kidney *qì* plays a fundamentally important role in the maintenance of good health, reproduction, and regeneration.

Shèn Zàng Tú: The kidney and its associated channel pathway, from *Zhēn Jiǔ Dà Chéng*.

Conversely, when the kidney *qì* is vacuous, that is, when the *jīng* stored in the kidney is weak, *yīn* and *yáng* fail to harmonize. The result is a vast variety of debilitating illnesses. Such illnesses are typical of elderly patients and include symptoms such as incontinence of urine, impotence, chronic low back pain, weakness in the knees, general debility, loss of memory, and other conditions that may typically be called "senile dementia" in the West.

As we noted at the beginning of our discussion of *qì* vacuity, it is a general condition that tends to affect the entire organism. Therefore, the foregoing comments related to the lungs, spleen, and kidney should be understood as interrelated. The diminished function of any one of these organic systems strongly affects the others, just as in biomedical physiology each of these function to support one another and maintain the proper operation of the whole organism.

It would not be possible to include in this chapter all the theoretical tools that doctors of Chinese medicine have at their disposal for the purpose of analyzing and understanding their patient's *qì*. We conclude, therefore, with a brief summary of various symptoms of disordered *qì* to show how practitioners approached the identification of what is going on when a patient presents in clinic.

The *qì* can become disordered in numerous ways: the lack of generation of *qì*, restraint of *qì*, exhaustion of *qì*, diminished function of *qì*, counterflow *qì* (reversed direction of *qì* flow), and various other disorders of the movement of *qì*. Many of these manifest in ways that are similar to the symptoms of *qì* vacuity described above. The following list of symptoms are all considered to be indicators of disordered *qì:*

Fever	Cough	Hiccups
Chills	Dyspnea	Vomiting
Spontaneous perspiration	Asthenic breathing	Diarrhea
Dizziness	Shortness of breath	Numbness
Deafness	Palpitations	Pain
Tinnitus	Insomnia	Frequent sighing
Fainting	Belching	

One last set of sensations that are important as indicators of *qì* are those experienced during acupuncture treatments. An essential phenomenon of acupuncture is known as *dé qì* 得氣, literally "obtaining *qì*." This refers to the immediate effect of inserting an acupuncture needle into an acupoint selected for treatment. The doctor administering the needle is attentive to the arrival of the *qì* (this patient- and practitioner-sensed sensation is another way to translate the expression *dé qì*), for if there is no distinct *dé qì* phenomenon, the treatment will have little if any effect. When the *qì* arrives at the needle, that is, when this *dé qì* phenomenon occurs, the patient may also experience one or more of the following sensations, depending on the depth and technique of needling employed.

The most common of these is a heavy, distended, or swollen feeling. This can be experienced as intense aching at the point of insertion. Often this sensation propagates along the channel to which the point being treated belongs. Other common *dé qì* sensations are: an electric sensation; itchiness; a feeling like ants crawling on the skin; and warmth. There are others, although these are the most common in China were stronger stimulation is typically the ideal. It is important for patients to understand the phenomenon and sensations of *dé qì,* as they must be able to inform the acupuncturist as to the results of needling. For some patients, until they are used to these sensations, the experience can be startling and a bit unpleasant, although treatment administered by a well-trained acupuncturist generally does not elicit pain during the course of therapy.

As we have seen, *qì* is among the most fundamental of traditional Chinese medical concepts. It serves as the medium through which the entire human organism interconnects and intercommunicates. In the theories and practices of Chinese medicine, the ancient philosophical concept of *qì* has developed into a manifold descriptor of both normal physiology and pathology. The images of the body, in both health and disease, which a doctor of Chinese medicine establishes and organizes during the course of diagnosis and treatment are characteristically integrated by a set of theoretical principles that assemble the body, the mind, and the physical environment into a series of micro- and macro-cosmic relationships. These are all understood and analyzed according to the pervasive notion of balance and harmony that springs directly from the philosophical sources we have discussed.

The resulting system of medical treatment and care is typified by a comprehensive, holistic, and anticipatory approach. This approach stems from the wisdom contained in the *Yellow Emperor's Classic of Internal Medicine*. The following passage reflects the gist of this wisdom.

> *In ancient times the sages did not treat patients who had already developed illness and symptoms; they did not try to rule those who had already become unruly. They chose instead to educate the people before they rose in rebellion. They preferred to treat their patients before they became ill. Treating patients who have symptoms of disease with needles and with herbs can be likened to the behavior of those who begin to forge their weapons after they are engaged on the field of battle. It is like those who only begin to dig a well after they have become thirsty. Aren't such actions just a little late?*

To a great extent, it is the comprehension of *qì* which has permitted this remarkable approach to health care to develop and flourish for more than 2000 years, just as it is an understanding of *qì* that can provide contemporary doctors and patients with a distinct advantage when confronting the challenges of health maintenance in the modern world.

Chapter 5

Qì Gōng

Early morning in most Chinese cities a curious ritual takes place. In parkways, on sidewalks, in private courtyards and public squares, people congregate in groups as small as two and as large as two hundred or more. They stand and swing their arms in circles, drawing the morning air inside themselves with sweeping gestures. Here, a group follows a leader through a cycle of movements that repeats again and again. There, on the next corner, a smaller group practices seemingly randomly. Yet there seems to be an internal coherence. Sometimes there is music. Often they practice in silence.

If you sleep late, you can find the same or similar rituals repeated in the afternoon. In People's Park, a woman stands with her arms extended as if she were trying to embrace the pine tree just before her. Off in a corner, an old man with half closed eyes stares to infinity. Stand and watch long enough and invariably someone, anyone, will approach you and in English that is occasionally fluent, often broken, yet always sincere, inform you that they are doing "deep breathing exercise—*qì gōng*." And, if you are interested, you can join in.

In recent years, *qì gōng* has been gaining an enormous popularity in China, as it has around the world. Practitioners consider it the *dào* of preserving life, a treasure from ancient times. Contemporary *qì gōng* masters claim followings that number in the hundreds of thousands, if not millions.

Not only are the followers of such masters legion, so are the myths and legends that have grown up around individuals supposed to possess "special skills." In numerous schools of *qì gōng* around China, something from the country's ancient cultural past is alive and flourishing. It is as if the magic of the ancient shaman reemerged in the midst of China's headlong rush to the twenty-first century.

Given the fundamental importance of *qì* in Chinese life, described in the foregoing chapters from different perspectives, it is understandable that since ancient times the Chinese have developed disciplines and practices for cultivating and refining their *qì*. In contemporary parlance, such disciplines are grouped under the heading, "*qì gōng.*" In ancient times, *qì gōng* was known by various names. According to Ma Ji Ren, a contemporary researcher, the term *qì gōng* 氣功 first appeared in the Jin Dynasty (265 C.E.–420 C.E.) in a Daoist text entitled *Records of the Clear Mirror of Religion* (*Míng Jìng Zhōng Jiào Lù*) by Xu Xun. However, in his book, *Chinese Qì Gōng* (*Zhōng Guó Qì Gōng*), Ma Ji Ren points out that this term was not in popular use until after 1949. One of those who contributed to its current use was Liu Gui Zhen. In 1957 he wrote a book entitled the *Practical Treatment Methods of Qì Gong* (*Jiǎn Yì Qì Gōng Zhì Liáo Fǎ*) in which he stated:

> *Why call it qì gōng? The word qì here represents breathing. Gōng is the practice of constantly adjusting the breathing and posture.*

In the 1982 revision of this same book, Liu Gui Zhen added,

> *According to the ancient classical theory, the name of this method of self-practice depends on the principle of fostering one's zhèng qì* 正氣 *[righteous qì] . . . I believe the word qì not only means the qì of breathing but includes the idea of the zhèng qì within one's body.*

Qì gōng 氣功 literally means "exercises for strengthening *qì*." The character *gōng* 功 is composed of the character 工 which means "work" or "labor" (which here lends both its sound and sense to the word 功) and the character *lì* 力 which means "strength" or "force." The composite meaning of these two characters is clearly "strength work," or as we have interpreted it here, "exercises for building strength." Add to this concept the complex significances of *qì*, and the meaning of *qì gōng* begins to emerge: exercise to strengthen the *qì*.

Qì gōng is a generic term that is used to describe a considerable variety of schools of thought and approaches to the practice of developing the *qì*. Like much of traditional Chinese culture, it is shrouded in mystery and veiled by an apocrypha that makes it difficult to develop a clear picture of its past. Contemporary teachers and practitioners share this tendency, and we must often satisfy ourselves with an obscure view of exactly what is happening today in Chinese *qì gōng* circles.

In this chapter we focus on those traditions of practice and cultivation which emphasize quiet sitting and/or standing exercise postures, the motionless varieties of *qì gōng* practice. In the next chapter we turn to those traditional practices which developed the movements of *qì* and use them to animate the entire body.

Section One: Ancient Roots and Practices

The origins of *qì gōng* are not precisely known. We can identify in the dances of prehistoric shaman or *wū* 巫 the ancient antecedents of both internal (i.e., mental) exercise and external movements conceived and executed for the purpose of influencing unseen powers. It is conceivable that among the Chinese there have been practitioners of some form or other of *qì gōng* since the dawn of civilization. The oldest coherent system of exercises designed to guide and cultivate *qì*, however, date to before the beginning of the imperial era of Chinese history. Among the ancient, extant descriptions of such methods, the earliest and most coherent comes from one of the preeminent Daoist philosophers of the Warring States period (475 B.C.E–221 B.C.E.).

In the Daoist classic of Zhuang Zi entitled *Kè Yì*, there are clear references to this early systematic method of developing the power of *qì* and harnessing its life-extending potentials. "One who practices *dǎo yǐn* [exercise to lead and guide the *qì*] to preserve one's health seeks to be like Peng Zu who excelled at longevity." He elaborates on this theme, providing a broad vision of the philosophical and moral foundations of health preservation practice.

Drawing of Daoist immortal Peng Zu, from the Ming Dynasty book *Liè Xiān Quān Zhuàn*.

The old saying is, "be indifferent to fame and gain; be alone in emptiness; repose in non-action." This is the basis of the balance of heaven and earth. It is likewise the highest extent of moral cultivation. Thus goes the saying that the sage remains within such limits and that one who can do so will meet only with things that are easily done without the slightest difficulty. Being comfortable and indifferent to fame and fortune, worry and illness will never intrude. The evil qì cannot penetrate. Thus virtue completes itself and the spirit will not be lost. Thus we say: to work ceaselessly will bring calamity upon the body. To constantly release the jīng 精 *[essence or semen] will result in strain or the relapse of disease due to fatigue. This leads eventually to exhaustion [of the jīng]. By nature, water is clear if it has no impurity. It stays calm if no force acts upon it. But if it stagnates it will not remain pure. This is a manifestation of the virtue of heaven and the basis of the ancient admonition to remain pure without the slightest impurity. Remain quiet and Oneness never changes. Be indifferent to fame and gain. Repose in non-action. Follow this law of heaven when motion is enforced. This is the dào of preserving the spirit.*

The Daoists placed supreme value on spiritual cultivation. Such cultivation was conceived as the highest level of harmonization with the great *dào* of nature. "Remain quiet and pure." "Repose in non-action." These are the fundamental principles of Daoist meditation. They lead directly to the practices of *dǎo yǐn*, the early antecedent of *qì gōng*. However, to understand how these practices developed through time, we must look more closely at the relationships between the Daoist world view and natural phenomena, the role of *qì*, and the preservation of health and long life.

Qì is the origin of both the form and substance of the whole universe. Everything is a result of *qì*. Humankind is thus understood as created by *jīng qì*. The space of the atmosphere is filled with the *qì* supplied by heaven to fulfill the human urge for respiration. The process of breathing was understood as the release of the old and the reception of the new. Ancient people clearly understood that breathing was an absolute requirement for life. They extended this awareness by comparing their own breathing with the rhythmic phases of natural phenomena. Nature itself was seen to breathe in and out, the tide came and went, the diurnal exchange of light and darkness endlessly cycled.

By contrasting human rhythms to the longer and lower frequencies of nature's rhythmic "breathing," the ancient Chinese people came to believe that lengthening their breath could extend their lives. As an expression of their understanding of the continuity that exists between humankind and nature, they began to practice exercises that concentrated on long, deep breathing. This ancient practice was known as *shí qì* 食氣 or "eating *qì*." It appears in one of the scrolls discovered at Ma Wang Dui known as "Abandon Grain and Eat *Qì*" (*Què Gŭ Shí Qì*).

Thus deep, quiet, lengthy breathing was a primary feature of *dăo yĭn* meditation. *Dăo yĭn* 導引 means "guiding" and "stretching." The character *dăo* 導 has several meanings, including: lead; guide; transmit; conduct; instruct; and teach. The character *yĭn* 引 means to draw (as one draws a bow); to stretch; to lead or guide; to leave, keep clear of, or make way for; to lure, attract, ensnare, or trap; to cause or make; to quote or make reference to. The overall sense of the phrase *dăo yĭn* can be easily understood, yet a question remains.

What is it that those who practiced this ancient form of meditative breathing were seeking to guide and draw out? The answer becomes clear because *dăo yĭn* is a method for conducting *qì* throughout the body, accumulating and cultivating *qì* to harmonize the practitioner with the forces of nature through the unseen but evident power of *qì*. The exercises were meant to conform with the principles Zhuang Zi expressed in the passage we cited earlier. Remain quiet. Repose in non-action. Let the *qì* be guided (導) by the movements of the *dào* (道) of nature.

Drawing of Peng Zhong, from the Ming Dynasty text *Liè Xiān Quán Zhuàn*.

Section Two: The Aims of *Qì Gōng* Practitioners

Today in China and around the world there are many schools of *qì gōng*. Some adhere closely to the ancient principles described in this section. Some have adopted other guidelines and seek to develop special skills. Here we will explore the various human objectives that *qì gōng* is used to achieve.

We begin with a look at medical *qì gōng*. Medical *qì gōng* consists of methods guided by medical theory and intended to help patients cure or prevent disease. Today, in most of the colleges and universities of traditional Chinese medicine in the People's Republic of China, there are departments, or at the very least, professors of *qì gōng*. It is recognized as a valid healing modality and enjoys widespread acceptance in both the traditional Chinese medical community and the general Chinese population. Although the precise mechanisms by which it works are as yet still not clearly understood in scientific terms, the results obtained from the practice of healing *qì gōng* have been thoroughly documented in numerous cases. There is, of course, extensive debate as to the meaning of such cases and their scientific validity. But a simple fact remains: thousands, perhaps tens or even hundreds of thousands of patients, have been beneficially treated using the methods of *qì gōng*.

Our look at *qì gōng* healing is meant neither as a critique nor as a justification. We are exploring *qì gōng* in the context of our broad investigation into the natural history of *qì*. There are numerous books, some of which report on scientific studies into *qì gōng* healing, and these are available to those who wish to investigate such matters more deeply.

Leaving aside, for the moment, the question of how such healing takes place, we can explore the aims of those who practice *qì gōng* healing. What are they trying to accomplish? What do they believe they are doing?

First and foremost there is the establishment of direct and sympathetic communication with the patient. Keep in mind that the phenomena Western medical doctors have consigned to the negatively-connoted phrase "placebo effect" has been an integral aspect of medicine in China for thousands of years. That is to say, the complete relationship that exists between physician and patient, including those aspects which medical science can not easily or clearly explain, are conscientiously included, in fact, embraced, by practitioners of each modality of traditional Chinese medicine. This reflects a fundamentally pragmatic approach to healing: if it works, use it.

Thus practitioners of *qì gōng* healing typically adopt as their first objective in any treatment the establishment of close and empathetic communication with the patient. They listen to what the patient has to say. They let the patient know that he or she has been heard and understood. They engage and involve the patient in the healing process, forming a close partnership.

One of the first actions of most *qì gōng* practitioners, once this healing partnership has been established, is to reassure the patient that healing can indeed take place. This appears to be an important objective because it encourages and assists the patient in overcoming the sense of despair and helplessness that often result from disease and suffering. Whether by training, intuition, or merely common sense, most of the *qì gōng* practitioners we have observed understand the importance of empathy to their healing practice.

The next general objective of *qì gōng* healers seems to be the extension of this bond between themselves and their patients by connecting their *qì*. This is done through different means, that is, in any given session of *qì gōng* therapy this step may look quite different to a non-participant observer. But the common aim is the establishment of a direct link with the patient so that the healer's *qì* can influence and guide the patient's *qì*. Sometimes it is done through physical contact of the practitioner's hands upon the patient's body. In other instances it is done with no direct physical contact.

Some practitioners seek to diagnose on the basis of determining where, how, and to what extent the patient's *qì* is obstructed or otherwise dysfunctional. Those who engage in such diagnoses do so in differing ways. It is not easy to simply characterize them. Many practitioners are loathe to reveal their methods. Others claim not to have any rational or coherent explanation for what they do, insisting instead that they are simply following a "feeling" or something even more vague.

Once a *qì gōng* practitioner has established a specific target or objective for treatment, the main aim becomes the transfer of *qì* from healer to patient. Again, this is done using a variety of postures and techniques. The phrase in Chinese is *fā qì* 發氣. Literally translated, it means "to issue or transmit *qì*." Since *qì* is by definition invisible, it is difficult to suppose what measurable event is actually occurring during such a transfer. Though *qì* is known as "insubstantial, like the mists that rise to form the clouds," it is also thought to contain "something vital that can be verified," according to Lao Zi. Indeed, patients who have been successfully treated by means of *qì gōng* will often claim that they received something vital from the healer.

Next, we turn to the aims of those who practice *qì gōng* as a method of maintaining health and extending life. What do these practitioners hope to accomplish through their daily regimen of breathing and meditation?

A primary objective is to relax and calm the mind. In fact, virtually every set of instructions we have ever heard or read begins with exactly this initial step. The practitioner is admonished to sit or stand quietly and relax the entire body and the mind. Some express this as trying to "clear" the mind of all thoughts. Others hold that even the effort to clear the mind is too much effort and that one must simply relax and allow the mind to behave as it will. Thoughts come and go like the breeze, and one must not be disturbed by these wisps of notions.

Drawing of Zhuang Bo Wei, from the Ming Dynasty book *Liè Xiān Quán Zhuàn*.

Regardless of the particular approach, the primary objective of *qì gōng* practice is to attain a state of mind that is quiet and calm. Such mental states have been correlated with various patterns of brain wave activity, but centuries before there were devices capable of monitoring and measuring the electrical state of the brain, *qì gōng* practitioners were capable of understanding when they had achieved this most basic step of their practice.

This first objective accomplished, the next aim of *qì gōng* practice is to become aware of the motion of *qì* within and without the body. The cultivation of a sensory awareness of *qì* is particularly difficult to describe. It varies from person to person. One individual may experience many different awarenesses of the presence and influence of *qì*. We cannot discount the possibility that some may invent sensations to assure themselves that their practice is progressing. We cannot prove that they are not wasting their time with stiff and sore legs. There is certainly no limit to the variety of experiences encountered during the course of such practice. Nonetheless, there does seem to be a common objective among most if not all *qì gōng* practitioners: to develop a sensitivity to the presence and movements of *qì*.

The various schools of *qì gōng* advise a wide variety of techniques to pursue and practice once one has become sensitive to *qì*. The common denominator of these practices is the development of an ability to exert mental influence over the movement of *qì* in the body. Some methods focus on gathering the *qì* in one or more bodily locations. Others begin by seeking to induce a particular pattern of *qì* circulation. In short, this step of *qì gōng* practice can be described as bringing the flow of *qì* under the conscious control of the practitioner.

Once in mental control of *qì*, a skill or state achieved by relatively few who set out to achieve it, the focus of *qì gōng* practice becomes even more esoteric and difficult to describe. More than 2500 years ago Lao Zi asked, "In concentrating the *qì* to attain resiliency, can you become like an infant?" The meaning of this question is not merely open to, but also demands individual interpretation. It seems pointless to speculate what can and cannot be achieved by "concentrating the *qì*" or "becoming like an infant" unless and until one has achieved the earlier stages of such a pursuit.

Nevertheless we can note that since ancient times, practitioners of *qì gōng* have sought more advanced goals. The writings of Daoist alchemists are replete with methods and formulas designed to create an "Elixir of Life" that would provide them with immortality. Through their esoteric meditative practices Buddhists seek to enter a state of awakening or enlightenment. For example, in the Dzongchen practice of Tibetan Buddhism the aim is to transform the corporeal body into a rainbow of colored light so that it can return to its eternal abode.

We next explore a peculiarly Chinese manifestation of the search for immortality to understand its importance in the traditions of *qì* and the practices that have evolved over the centuries to cultivate and refine it.

Section Three: *Qì Gōng* and the Ancient Search for the Internal Elixir

Owing in large part to the long duration of Chinese civilization, *qì gōng* is both the ancestor and descendant of a practice that developed in the Sui and Tang dynasties (581 C.E.–907 C.E.) among the Daoist alchemists. According to Li Yuan Gui, a contemporary scholar of *qì gōng:*

> *The predecessor of the internal elixir is the qì method, which means the method of exercising the breath. The highest level of this qì method is called the internal elixir.*

An anonymous text from the Tang Dynasty entitled *Secluded Secrets of the Tang* (*Táng Yōu Jué*) states:

> *Qì can maintain life. This is the internal elixir. Medicine that can strengthen the physical form is called external elixir.*

The practices of exercising the *qì* that were already ancient in the Tang Dynasty were codified and refined into the art of the internal elixir, and over the ensuing centuries, the practices of Daoist alchemists who sought to discover and actualize this *qì*-based method of prolonging life have provided extensive materials for successive generations of *qì gōng* practitioners. The aim of the Daoist, however, was not simply to prolong life. Through the practices that came to be known as the "internal elixir," they sought to overcome the limits of mortality itself, attaining eternal life.

Nèi Jīng Tú, The Internal View. Painting from the Qing Imperial Court Museum.

The quest for immortality is certainly not unique to the Chinese. It is the lot of human beings to long for release from mortality and to seek an escape from death. Thus, what we see in the ancient traditions such as the search for the internal elixir is a Chinese expression of this fundamental human urge. To understand how the ancient Chinese fashioned this expression, we must first examine the meaning of the term "internal elixir."

As is evident in the anonymous quotation previously cited, Daoist alchemists conceived of two separate and distinct yet interrelated methods by which they hoped to discover a way to circumvent aging and death, achieving immortality and maintaining the strength of their physical bodies. The ultimate aim of these ancient experimenters was eternal life. We use the word alchemist to describe them because, like their counterparts in Europe of the Middle Ages, they were not content to believe that life eternal could be achieved through religious faith alone. They sought specific substances and methods to void the certainty of death and arrive at the ultimate achievement of eternal life—without dying.

Drawing of Zhang Zhong, from the Ming Dynasty book *Liè Xiān Quán Zhuàn.*

The first of these methods was the synthesis of herbal, animal, and mineral ingredients into a wide variety of concoctions that could be eaten, drunk, inhaled, or otherwise consumed. These "external elixirs" were formulated according to elaborate recipes, most of which were jealously guarded secrets. Unfortunately for those who took them, many of the formulas included highly toxic substances such as mercury. The frequent result, far from immortality, was certain death, either sudden or long and lingering.

The second method was to synthesize such an elixir of life without the use of foreign agents, relying upon the body's intrinsic substances and energies. This "internal elixir" was conceived of as a "golden elixir" that could be created slowly over years of continuous practice applying the principles of *dǎo yǐn* described in the preceding section. In fact, the synthesis of the internal elixir was—and is—the ultimate aim of those who practice these Daoist meditations.

Among the various traditions of Daoist practice that have flourished and vanished through the centuries, there are also those that combined both the internal and external methods. Although the distinction between them has become blurred with the passage of time, it is still possible to distinguish the essential difference we have just described. In addition, there was a search for herbal concoctions that could prolong life indefinitely that has been of tremendous significance in the development of Chinese herbal medicine.

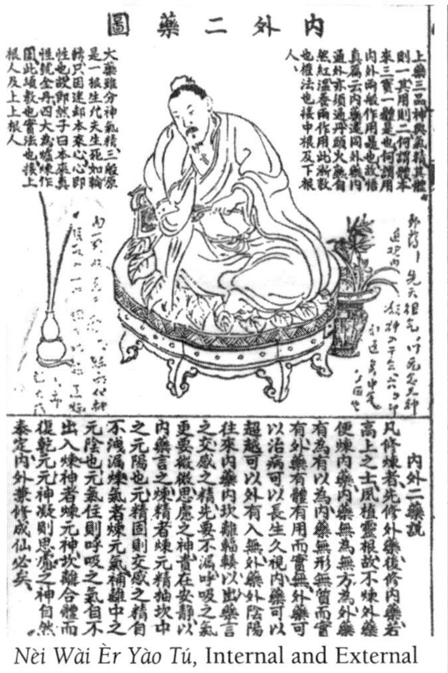

Nèi Wài Èr Yào Tú, Internal and External Medicine Diagram. From *Xìng Mìng Guī Zhǐ,* a Ming Dynasty Daoist text on internal elixir.

Certain of the medicinals common in modern traditional practice are known because of these alchemical investigations.

Our purpose, to reveal the cumulative significances that have attached themselves to the concept of *qì* throughout the centuries, is best served by an exploration of the search for the internal elixir, for *qì* was one of the primary ingredients required to synthesize this "golden elixir." The Daoists theorized that an admixture of *jīng* 精 (essence), *qì* 氣, and *shén* 神 could be created within the body using these three inborn bodily "treasures" as the primary ingredients. We say "primary ingredients" because the Daoists recognized that to accomplish this feat, they also needed air, food, and water. Thus dietary regulation was an important adjuvant to practices aimed at creating the internal elixir, as was regulation of the adepts' sexual lives.

In fact, to engage in this search for eternal life through regulation, accumulation, cultivation, and refinement of the body's inherent substances and energies, one had to adopt a lifestyle that was completely devoted to it. It was, in large part, the adherence to this lifestyle that lead the Daoist to withdraw from the civilized world and seek a place in nature where they could work undisturbed. A thorough indoctrination in the principles of the *dào* as contained in the various classics on the subject was also necessary to proceed. Only once these various preconditions of education, lifestyle, and diet were established and maintained could the work proceed.

We have described the early stages of such work in the foregoing section. To summarize, they consist of firstly calming the body and the mind; next, regulating the breath; then becoming sensitized to the movements of *qì;* and finally bringing the *qì* within the control of the conscious mind. The next steps led far beyond the realm of the ordinary. They required years of diligence and uninterrupted practice. They also required an intimate familiarity with a schema of the human body that revealed, to those who could decipher it, the precise locations where the *jīng,* the *qì,* and the *shén* could be accumulated and transformed into the internal elixir.

The name given to such locations was *dān tián* 丹田. This means "field of the elixir," and there were three such fields within the body. The first, or upper *dān tián*, is located in the head and corresponds roughly to the location of the pineal gland, between and slightly above the two eyes at the acupoint known as "Hall of Impressions," *yìn táng*. The second, or middle *dān tián,* is located in the chest, directly between the breasts on a line that connects the centers of the nipples at the acupoint named *shān zhōng,* "Chest Center," CV-17, the meeting point of *qì* for the spleen, kidney, small intestine, triple burner, and conception vessels. It is alternately known as "Chest Hall" (a gathering place), "The Source," "The Upper Sea of *Qì*," and "Original Child," names which emphasize its function as a gathering place of *qì*. The third, or lower *dān tián* is located approximately one and one-third inches below the navel and approximately three-sevenths of the distance between the anterior and posterior surfaces of the body at the level of the acupoint known as *qì hǎi*, "Sea of Qi," CV-6.

In some versions of this schematic, the upper *dān tián* is known as the Palace of *Shén*, the middle *dān tián* as the Palace of *Qì*, and the lower *dān tián* as the Palace of *Jīng*. There are numerous texts on this subject and the techniques recommended for the use of each of these locations varies from source to source. What follows is a summary of the methods common to numerous sources.

The name of the practice or art of the internal elixir appeared sometime during the span of the Sui and Tang Dynasties (581 C.E.–907 C.E.). Like so much of Chinese philosophy and traditional arts and sciences, it was refined and developed into applicable procedures during the Song Dynasty (960 C.E.–1279 C.E.). During the successive periods of the Jin, Yuan, Ming, and Qing Dynasties (1115 C.E–1911 C.E.), it took on the highly specialized form most often associated with the concept, becoming a whole system with special theories and practices. The roots of this unique method of cultivating the *qì*, however, can be found in texts that date from the Eastern Han period (25 C.E.–220 C.E.).

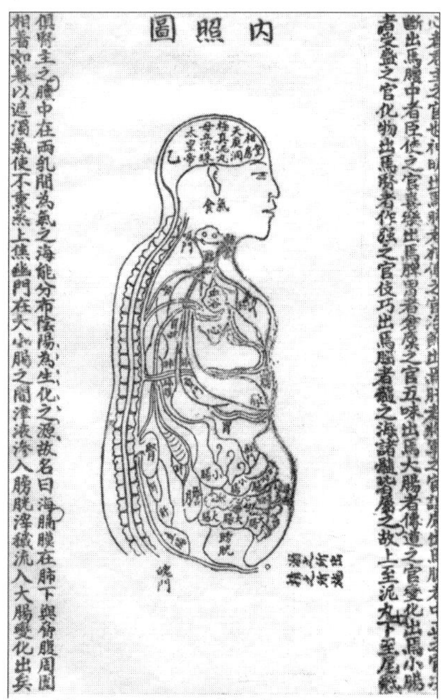

Nèi Zhào Tú, Internal Reflection Diagram. From *Xìng Mìng Guī Zhǐ*, a Ming Dynasty Daoist text on internal elixir.

Drawing of Wei Bo Yang, from the Ming Dynasty book *Liè Xiān Quán Zhuàn*.

Wei Bo Yang, who was a famous Daoist of the Eastern Han, authored a work entitled *Concordance of "Three" in the Book of Changes* (*Zhōu Yì Cān Tóng Qì*), which is perhaps the earliest classic of *qì gōng* practice. It consists of three volumes which expound a theoretical foundation for the cultivation of *qì* based upon the images and mystical mathematics of the *Zhōu Yì* 周易 or *Yì Jīng* 易經, the *Book of Changes*. The essence of this approach was to regulate the motion of the *jīng* and *qì* so that they conformed with the alternations of *yīn* and *yáng* described by the changing images or hexagrams, the *guà* 卦 of the *Yì Jīng*.

In the Sui Dynasty (581 C.E.–618 C.E.), when the Daoist Su Yuan Lang referred to the practices of regulating the motions of *jīng* and *qì* according to the ancient principles of *dǎo yǐn* as the art of the internal elixir, that name stuck. As described above, it served to identify a tradition of cultivation that developed slowly over the next several hundred years. The theory of the internal elixir has since had three main characteristics.

The first was the traditional worldview that integrated heaven, earth, and humankind into a unity and featured the notion of macro- and micro-cosmic relationships interconnecting human beings with the *qì* of heaven and earth. The second main characteristic was the absorption of certain aspects of China's other two leading religions, Buddhism and Confucianism. Of particular import was the Confucian ideal of the "upright heart and sincere mind," which became prerequisites to the practice of the internal elixir. From Buddhism the meditative technique known as *zhǐ guān* 止觀 (literally, "stop vision") was incorporated into the practice of the internal elixir. This technique, perhaps most widely recognized in the West as the practice of Zen meditation, stresses the importance of highly concentrated consciousness, focused on an object or vision held steadfastly in the mind. In its highest stages, as in the ultimate step of the internal elixir described following, this "object" of concentration is the Great Void, *tài xū* 太虛.

The third important characteristic of the practice of the internal elixir was the step-by-step method to be followed as one progressed through years of practice. The process of synthesizing the internal elixir was divided into four major steps. We summarize them here and will review them again at the end of this section after having considered the salient points of each.

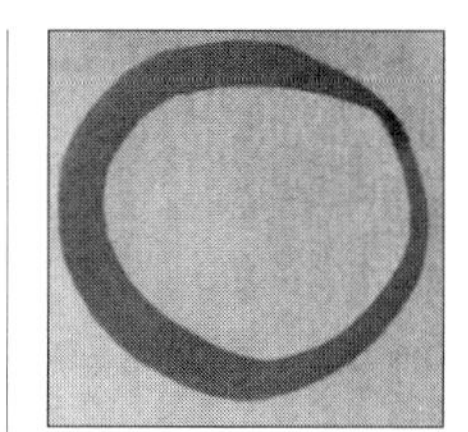

Tài xū, the Great Void

1. Preparation, known as "building the vessel and readying the burner." This step consists of relaxing mind and body. Breathing is slowly regulated and brought under conscious control. The *qì* is accumulated in the *dān tián*. This accumulation takes place over a prolonged period. A series of methods for guiding and drawing the *qì* throughout the body are practiced in an established sequence to develop the special potentials of these various bodily locations.

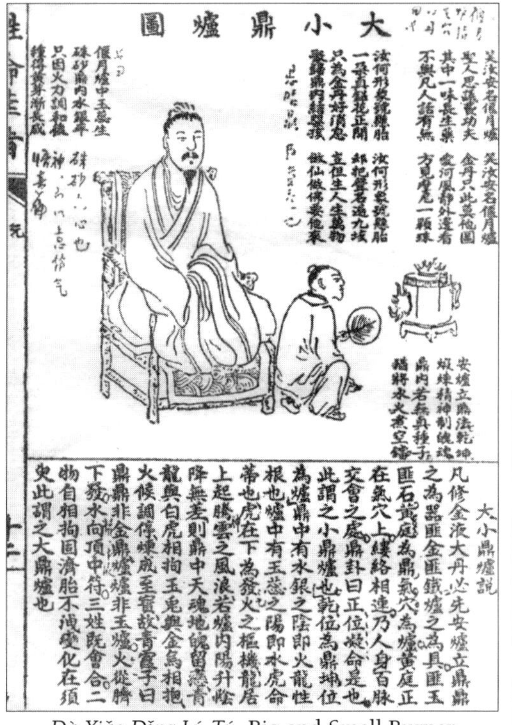

Dà Xiǎo Dǐng Lú Tú, Big and Small Burner Diagrams. From the *Xìng Mìng Guī Zhǐ*, a Ming Dynasty Daoist text on internal elixir.

2. Once preparation is complete, the practitioner proceeds to the steps known as "refining and transforming the *jīng* into *qì*." This is one of the primary aims of internal Daoist alchemy. It involves conservation and accumulation of the *jīng* which is closely associated with carefully controlled sexual practices and the retention of semen. Through the initial preparation and accumulation of *jīng*, the practitioner is made ready to proceed with the transformation of *jīng* into *qì* through a series of visualization and breathing exercises.

3. The third step of the process is "refining and transforming the *qì* into *shén*." As the adept progresses these steps become more arcane and difficult to grasp. But what is taking place is clearly a process of rarefaction or ephemeralization, whereby the substantive energies and essential substances that constitute the living organism are transformed to increasingly less substantial states. This

process is thought to powerfully and positively influence health and to result in longevity.

Drawing of the Daoist immortal Huan Kai, from the book *Liè Xiān Quán Zhuàn* from the Ming Dynasty.

4. The final stage is "return the *shén* to the Great Void." This is the ultimate extension of the process of ephemeralization of the body's essential substances. In the illustrations contained within Daoist texts on the subject, the adept who achieves this step is pictured flying to heaven on the back of a white crane.

The practice of arts of the internal elixir that were based upon the ideas of Tang Dynasty (618 C.E.–907 C.E.) alchemists reached their peak during the later Song and Yuan Dynasties (960 C.E.–1368 C.E.). During this period the theories and methods of internal elixir practice were articulated in detail by a variety of schools. Different schools emphasized different aspects of the practice. Later, during the Ming and Qing Dynasties (1368 C.E.–1911 C.E.), the art of the internal elixir took on the status of the leading, most advanced of *qì gōng* practices. This was due largely to the difficulty of its methods and the long study and practice it required. It was also due to the cumulative effects of the traditional method of teaching and transmission of such arts in China. Traditional transmission took the form of a master teaching a few of his most advanced disciples. Masters would frequently withhold certain critical aspects of their teaching to ensure the safety of their students. These techniques are believed to be potentially dangerous if practiced wrongly or by a student who is not adequately prepared.

This method of transmission tends to obscure the contents of the teaching as it passes from generation to generation. But this was countered by a contrary tendency to produce a literature on the subject that was simply expressed in the common parlance of the day—this as a way of counteracting the "secrecy" of the traditional teaching methods. Additionally, doctors and common people began to look for other ways of practicing and developing *qì gōng* to incorporate it into medical practice and daily life. Many of these "new" *qì gōng* practices absorbed whatever they could of the traditional internal elixir teachings, giving rise to the development of hybrid systems of *qì gōng*.

To more fully understand and appreciate the meaning and importance of the internal elixir in the history and development of the *qì* concept, it is important to investigate several key terms and phrases that appear in the ancient literature devoted to the subject. Below we discuss seven of these critical components of the nomenclature of the internal elixir and of *qì gōng* in general.

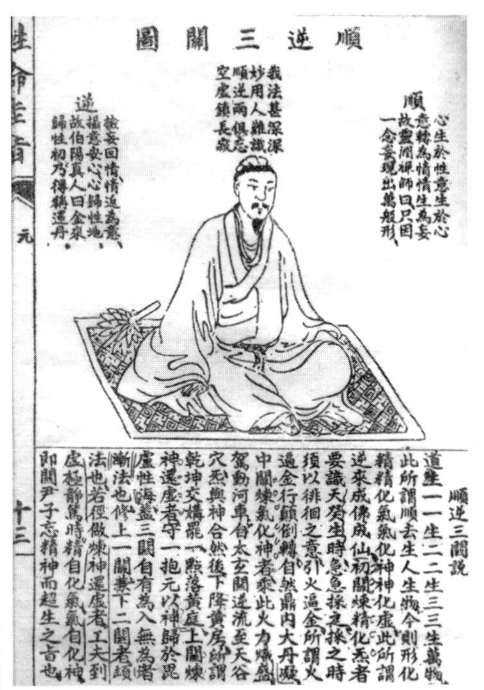

Shùn Nì Sān Guān Tú, Three Gates Diagram. From the *Xìng Mìng Guī Zhǐ*, a Ming Dynasty Daoist text on internal elixir.

I. The Three Treasures

Sān Bǎo 三寶, *Jīng* 精, *Qì* 氣, *and Shén* 神

These are sometimes referred to as the "Three Origins." In the Yuan Dynasty (1279 C.E.–1368 C.E.), a Daoist named Cheng Zhi Xu describing the internal elixir wrote, "Its functional contents are *jīng, qì, shén*. Its name is the Golden Elixir."[1] *Jīng, qì*, and *shén* are the primary ingredients of the internal elixir. According to a contemporary Daoist book entitled *Teaching Materials on the Inscription from the Classic of the Yellow Court* (*Huáng Tíng Jīng Jiǎng Yī*):

[1] "Golden Elixir" is another term used to refer to the internal elixir. This usage results from two different aspects: the relationship between the practices of the internal and external elixirs; and the metaphorical meaning of metal in Chinese symbology. Daoist alchemists seeking external elixirs often included various metals in their formulas and compounds. The Chinese word for metal is *jīn* which also means "gold." In fact, Daoist alchemists sought both internal and external elixirs, and struggled with formulas and practices of various kinds to synthesize a whole approach to ingestion of medicinals and exercisesof the mind and body in order to formulate a "golden pill," which phrase equates with immortality.

Jīng, qì, shén as the basic elements of life have been widely discussed since the Spring and Autumn period (770 B.C.E.–476 B.C.E.), but to merge these three into a unity, to study and research this unity, is a special characteristic of Daoism. In the study of the internal elixir, these three are intimately linked as supplements of one another. They cannot be separated. The original shén is the commander. It is the key to success in the internal elixir. The shén rules over the qì and thereby refines the jīng.

2. The Three Passes
Sān Guān 三關

During the step-by-step progress in the overall practice of formulating the internal elixir, the *qì* moves along the *dū mài* 督脉 channel that follows the spine from the perineum, over the top of the head, to the tongue. As it moves it passes through three important "gates" or "passes" known as *wěi lǔ guān* 尾閭關: the coccyx; a series of 17 bilateral acupuncture points located along the lumbar and thoracic spine (*jiā jǐ guān* 夹脊關); and "Jade Pillow Pass" (*yù zhěn guān* 玉枕關), located in the occipital region. These are known as the three passes on the back. There are also three passes on the front of the body known as *ní wán* 泥丸: the point at the top of the head, here referring to the brain or the spirit of the brain; *jiàng gōng* 絳宮, the "Crimson Palace" (i.e., the heart); and the *xià dān tián* 下丹田, the Lower Elixir Field.

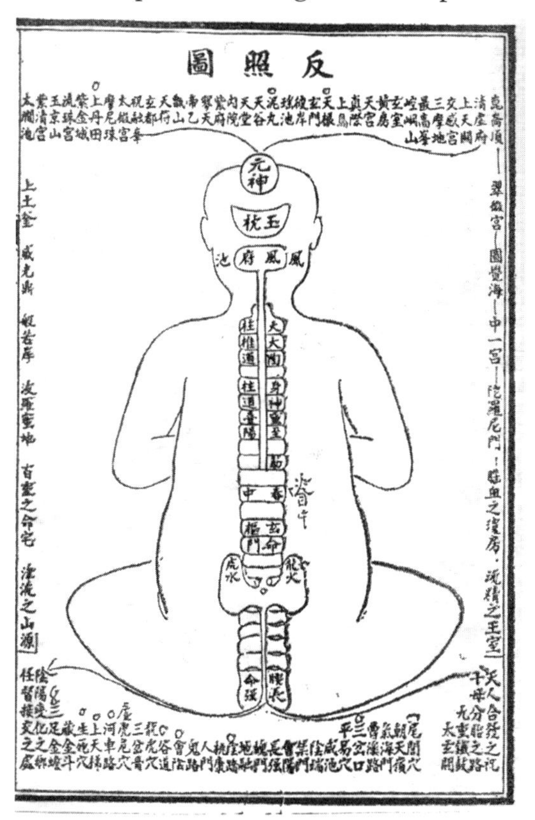

Fǎn Zhào Tú, Posterior Reflection Diagram. From the *Xìng Mìng Guī Zhǐ*, a Ming Dynasty Daoist text on internal elixir.

3. The Vessel and the Burner

Dǐng Lú 鼎爐

In the art of the internal elixir these terms refer to relative positions in the body used to refine the *jīng* and *qì*. The terms are, again, borrowings from the practices and artifacts associated with the alchemy of the Golden Elixir. They are literary references to the burners and vessels employed by the Daoist alchemists to mix and heat their longevity compounds.

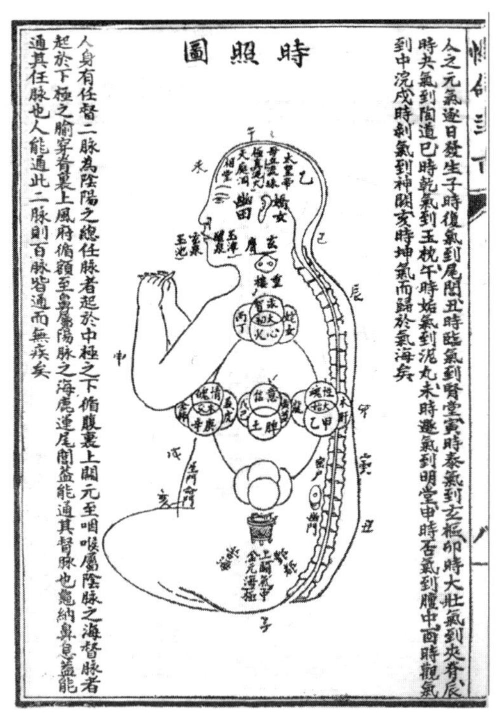

Shí Zhào Tú, Time Reflection Diagram. From the *Xìng Mìng Guī Zhǐ*, a Ming Dynasty Daoist text on internal elixir.

There are two sets of vessels and burners applied to the development of the internal elixir: the Big Vessel and Burner and the Little Vessel and Burner. When the vessel is positioned at *ní wán* (inside the head) and the burner is located in the lower *dān tián,* the meaning and the result is that the *qì* is guided to travel through the three passes on the back along the *dū mài* to *ní wán.* It then returns through the three front passes to the lower *dān tián.* This process is referred to as the Big Vessel and Burner. It is used during the second step of the process of the internal elixir, that is, the refining and transforming of the *jīng* into *qì.*

When the vessel is positioned in the heart and the burner is located in the lower *dān tián*, the *qì* guards the *shén* between those two locations. In this instance it is not circulated through either the *dū mài* or through the *rèn mài* (the channel running along the anterior midline of the body which is the *yīn* compliment of the *yáng, dū mài*). This is known as the Small Vessel and Burner. It is used in the third step of the internal elixir to refine the *qì* and transform it into *shén.*

4. The River Chariot
Hé Chē 河車

This term refers to the *qì* in motion along the *rèn mài* and the *dū mài.* When the movement of *qì* follows the Small Heavenly Circle and the Big Heavenly Circle (See terms 5 and 6 following), the practitioner refers to this as the movement of the river chariot. Note that here we see the extended metaphor of the circulation of *qì* considered as the water pathway connecting the whole body.

5. The Small Heavenly Circle
Xiǎo Zhōu Tiān 小周天

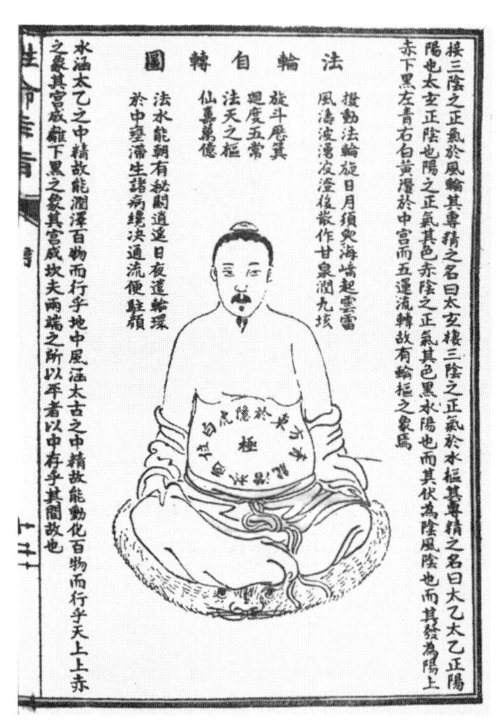

Fá Lún Zì Zhuàn Tú, Self-turning Wheel of the Law Diagram. From The *Xìng Mìng Guī Zhǐ*, a Ming Dynasty Daoist text on internal elixir.

This phenomenon is sometimes referred to as "before the pass." It applies to the second step of the internal elixir, the refining and transforming of *jīng* into *qì*. The main action consists of guiding the inborn *jīng* in a meditative state and mobilizing it 360 times according to the movement of the river chariot. This process consists of four stages. First is "gathering the medicine," the original or inborn *jīng* or essence. This can only be done in a state of complete and profound relaxation. It cannot be accomplished through the slightest mental force. The next step is to "seal the medicine," send it to the lower *dān tián* where it is stored. The third step is to "refine the medicine." This consists of 360 cycles of breathing and circulating the *qì* in the *rèn mài* and *dū mài.* The fourth and final step is to stop the motion of the river chariot after it has circulated 360 times. The practitioner then "sees" the sun rays three times. At this point the true *yáng* congeals and the Big Medicine is produced. The practitioner must stop at this point or there will be a repletion of *yáng* fire. Some schools stress that a fourth rising of the sun is to be conscientiously avoided. This reflects the danger inherent in over-stimulating *yáng qì*. This process takes 100 days to complete and is sometimes known as the "Hundred Day Pass."

6. The Big Heavenly Circle
Dà Zhōu Tiān 大周天

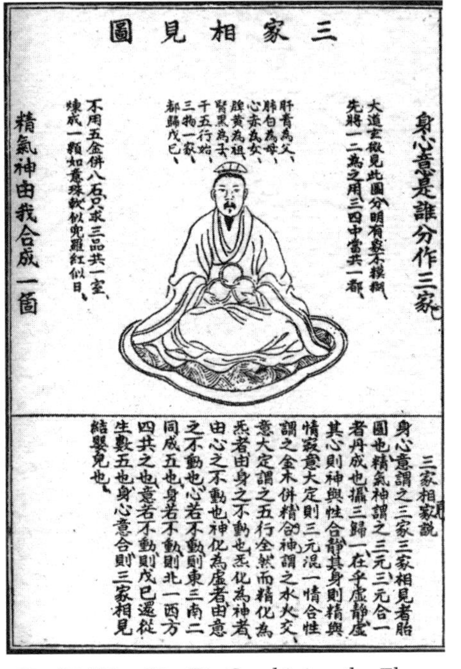

Sān Jiā Xiāng Jiàn Tú, Combining the Three Treasures Diagram. From the *Xìng Mìng Guī Zhǐ,* a Ming Dynasty Daoist text on internal elixir.

This term applies to the third step of refining and transforming the *qì* into *shén.* The purpose of this step is to unify the *shén* and *qì,* thereby transforming the two to one. In this process the vessel is located in the middle *dān tián* and the burner is located in the lower *dān tián.* The original *qì* does not circulate through the *rèn* or *dū mài.* Instead it spreads like an enshrouding mist between these two locations. The practitioner is cautioned not to allow the mind to fix on either point.

The Big Heavenly Circle is sometimes referred to as "preserving the fetus." It constitutes a distinct form of *qì gōng* practice by itself. In terms of the internal elixir, the Small Heavenly Circle is understood as the action phase; the Big Heavenly Circle is understood as the non-action phase. To transform the *qì* (which in its natural state is always in motion) to *shén,* the *qì* must be brought to a state of motionlessness. In other words, it must be completely sublimated. In this state, the function of consciousness is to become without consciousness. The Chinese term for this is *wú jué* 無覺. This is a high level of the art of the internal elixir that develops motionless meditation to preserve the *shén* and to refine the original nature.

7. Fetus

Tāi 胎

This word is used to refer to the internal elixir itself, that is, the alchemical admixture of *jīng*, *qì*, and *shén*. The Ming Dynasty Daoist (1368 C.E.–1644 C.E.), Wu Shu Yang, explained this in his *Direct Discussion of the Orthodox Theory of the Heavenly Being* (*Tiān Xiān Zhèng Lǐ Zhí Lùn*):

> *The foetus in qì gōng is the shén qì. It is not an image of an actual foetus. It has neither shape nor manifestation. To refine the elixir, first mix the shén and the qì. Later the qì is used to wrap and protect the shén. It is just like the foetus in the womb wrapped in the placenta. It does not inhale and exhale, but it still breathes. The manifestations of life and death yet exist. In and out remain intact. The internal elixir is just like the condition when the foetus is about to be born. Thus the image of the foetus is used to name it. It is created during the period when the practice proceeds from the stage of refining the jīng and transforming it into qì to the stage of refining the qì and transforming it into shén. It bears fruit in the lower dān tián and after seven days of refining in the circular pathway, it then becomes the foetus.*

The literature on the internal elixir is extensive. It contains many other terms and phrases that provide aspects important for understanding *qì* as well as a host of other key concepts in Chinese philosophy and culture. There are also many more detailed and complex instructions and admonitions, for example, adjusting the practice with the cyclical phases of the passing days, months, and years. One final note that applies not just to the issue of the correct timing of such practice but to every detail of every step is that to proceed effectively and successfully, a practitioner must be orally taught, that is, instructed by a teacher who has mastered the process and can give adequate instructions face to face. Without such instruction and guidance, the vagaries of individual interpretation and misapprehension can lead to failure. Failure can take many forms. The pursuit of such techniques is not without considerable risks. One is, after all, seeking to manipulate the very essences of life itself. The mind has many self-protecting mechanisms, however. Those who find the art of the internal elixir outlandish or incredible are well-advised to stay away.

For those who find such an undertaking intriguing and would seek to find a qualified teacher and pursue this ancient, esoteric path, we can only offer our best wishes. We aim neither to encourage nor discourage. We simply wish to shed some light on this fascinating dimension of the history of *qì*. It can only help those who wish to develop a clearer understanding of the many systems and approaches to *qì gōng* practice that are growing rapidly in the West today.

Section Four: The Real and the Fake

It is sad but unavoidable that we must mention the many charlatans and scam artists who populate the world of *qì gōng*. Any such mention tends to take on the color of hostile derision, but it is not our intention to engage in name calling or finger pointing. In fact, we do not consider ourselves masters of the subject; thus we cannot authenticate the claims or methods of any individual or group purveying *qì gōng*. Therefore you will not find a directory of valid and/or invalid schools of *qì gōng*. Nonetheless, we would do you a disservice if we omitted mention of the fact that many of the people purveying special skills as *qì gōng* teachers and healers are, sadly, nothing of the sort. It is thus now, as it has thus been in Chinese history, and separating the fake from the real is the first task of the student.

Obviously, there are considerable difficulties when it comes to documentation, let alone proof of the existence of *qì* as a definable, quantifiable substance or force. Efforts to measure its healing properties encounter what are at present insurmountable difficulties. Certainly any such attempt is well beyond the capabilities of any individual. We are aware of a series of studies undertaken at the Beijing Academy of Sciences during the 1980s which attempted to document the skills of a several *qì gōng* practitioners and thereby "prove" their abilities as well as the existence of the very medium in which they profess to function. However, the consensus we have gleaned from colleagues both in China and the United States who are familiar with the reports from such studies, is that they fall short of their goal. As of this writing, there are no conclusive scientific studies that either prove or disprove the existence of *qì* or the special abilities that some *qì gōng* masters may advertise.

To us this does not mean that such things do not exist. To the contrary, the lack of such scientific evidence is, in itself, evidence of another set of phenomena. These phenomena to which we refer could be described as the gap between two disparate systems of thought and practice, the age-old chasm between East and West. This long-standing cultural gap need not endure forever. Our own speculations regarding the future of *qì* as a valid concept outside of its original Chinese context are contained in Chapter 7, following. For now, let it suffice for us to offer readers this gentle warning: *caveat emptor*—let the buyer beware. The marketplace is full of people offering various wares. It may not be possible to "kick the tires" of a vehicle as mysterious and invisible as *qì*, but within the confines of common sense, there are surely adequate safeguards to protect the well-intentioned from falling prey to those who seek only to free them of their hard-earned pay.

Perhaps one of the primary requirements for anyone who wishes to pursue a serious study of *qì* is the intelligence to be able to discern the real from the fraudulent. We cannot speculate further than to point out that for the past several thousand years, those who are sincere have been able to make progress, despite—indeed, perhaps, because of—many difficulties and hindrances.

Chapter 6

Qì in the Martial Arts

Students give up the immediate to seek the exotic; they don't understand the sheer marvelous function of the ch'i accumulating in the tan t'ien. The ch'i is just like wind, water, and clouds. They each can store power as the universe itself stores the primal ch'i.

—from *Cheng Tzu's Thirteen Treatises on T'ai Chi Ch'uan*

In the mid-1960s, years before the first "ping-pong diplomats" traveled between China and the United States, the cultural gap between China and the West was breached by a few Chinese boxers. Foremost among these was a young fighter whose name is still spoken in reverential tones on both sides of the Pacific: Li Xiao Long, Bruce Lee. The impact of his kicks and punches was surpassed only by the sheer force of his image on TV and theater screens. As Kato on TV's Green Hornet, he provided many Americans with their first glimpse of the Chinese martial arts. His mysterious death at the height of stardom only burned the image he left behind into the imagination of generations of his fans and students of the martial arts. Nowhere is the power of *qì* more mysterious, more provocative, or more magnetically attractive than in the art of fighting.

In the previous chapter, we explored several traditions of *qì gōng* 氣功 which primarily featured motionless, meditative practices to accumulate and cultivate *qì*. Strictly speaking, the subjects covered in this chapter are likewise aspects of *qì gōng*, in that they evolved from the same general principles and share the same aims. The difference between the material presented here and in Chapter 5 is that these disciplines focus on the concentration of *qì* in developing athletic and martial skill. However, this is not to say that the various martial arts or *wǔ shù* 武术 do not possess important meditative and spiritual dimensions.

In fact, the martial arts in China have a profoundly spiritual nature. From a pragmatic point of view, the main distinction that can be made between the martial arts and the motionless methods of *qì gōng* is that the various martial arts were developed throughout Chinese history by certain individuals and groups who needed to defend themselves against attack.

In contemporary times, although people certainly still come under physical attack, the martial aspect of *wǔ shù* tends to work in a more metaphorical way. That is, the metaphoric context of defending oneself against an imaginary attacker provides the practitioner with a rationale whereby various principles of anatomy, physiology, and kinesthetics become clearly and intensely focused. But as we suggest, this martial focus in no way cancels or diminishes the meditative and spiritual aspects. In fact, for many who practice the martial arts described in this chapter, the metaphor of fighting for survival brings the spiritual dimension into vivid relief.

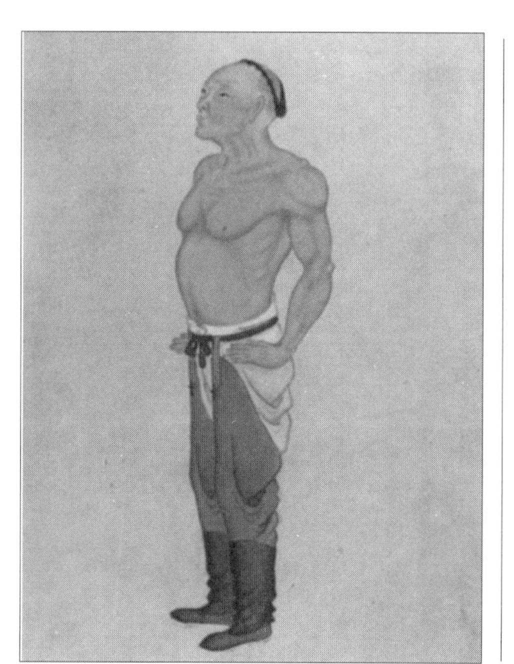

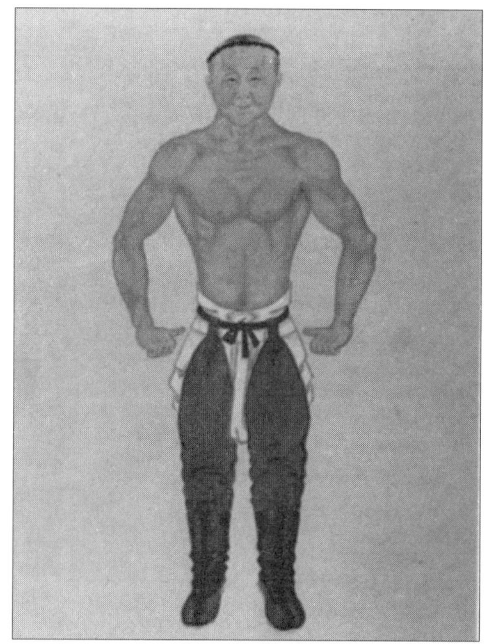

Illustrations of postures to adjust the *qì* for the practice of the external elixir. From *Tiáo Qì Liàn Wài Dān Tú Shì*, Qing Dynasty. Author unknown.

Naturally, the practice of martial arts also consists of actual combat as well as rigorous physical training to prepare the practitioner to deal effectively with the realities of physical attack. But ask most practitioners of Chinese *wǔ shù* what the main elements of their practice are, and more often than not you will hear "to develop the *qì*." We have separated these subjects into two chapters primarily as a convenience of presentation and not to suggest that there is a categorical difference between the subjects discussed.

Section One: The Power of *Qí*

All martial arts in China share one central focus: the development of the individual's *qì* to attain power. In Section Three, following, we discuss two different schools or branches of the traditional fighting arts of China, the internal and the external. Though they differ significantly in many aspects, they share this central concern for the development of *qì*.

The first thing that one must recognize about the power of *qì* is that, though obviously related to the strength and dexterity of the muscles, it is an altogether different quantity than muscular strength. The power of *qì* is inseparable from the development of the power of mental concentration and the ability to focus the mind—and the *qì*—in a particular movement, at a precise location, in a given moment. There are many experiences and events in the life and training of martial artists that exemplify this power. The following story is such an example.

One day in the summer of 1993, we were sitting in the clinic of Chen Wan Chuan, an old man who was both a doctor of traditional Chinese medicine and a teacher of martial arts. In Chengdu his family had been renowned as martial artists for generations. Prior to 1949 his father owned and operated a prestigious academy of *wǔ shù* located in the prosperous downtown neighborhood of Tai Sheng Lu. Dr. Chen himself had been a student of the late *tài jí quán* master Li Ya Xuan, the senior disciple of the great Yang Cheng Fu.

It was hot that August afternoon. The cooling effect of the morning rain had long since evaporated. A thick steamy mist hung in the air. We sat drinking tea and telling stories with Dr. Chen and his granddaughter, everyone doing their best to ignore the sweltering heat. Suddenly we heard a woman's voice cry out, "Thief! Thief!" The screaming woman appeared in

Yang Cheng Fu

Li Ya Xuan

Chen Wan Chuan

the entrance of the clinic. Her eyes bulged. Her arms flailed at the air. A young man ran by so quickly that it was hard to get a glimpse of him. We barely had a chance to react when Dr. Chen sprang from his stool and bolted out the door. He gave chase to the thief and by the time we had emerged from the front of the clinic, the two of them were nearly a hundred meters down the street.

We watched in amazement as Dr. Chen collared the young hoodlum and literally dragged him backwards as he still clung to the woman's purse. When he had managed to bring him back to the scene of his crime, he glowered at him until the thief handed the woman back her bag. Then he held him firmly with one hand and slapped the back of his head hard enough so that the sound echoed in the clinic. He bitterly cursed him with a few well chosen words, bitten off at their ends as if the words were poisonous snakes. Then he suddenly released his grip on the young man and jettisoned him forward with a snap that set him to running again. The would-be thief didn't stop running until he was out of view.

Dr. Chen came back into his clinic with a sly smile on his face. He was barely breathing hard. "What is this world coming to?" he asked in a philosophic tone. Then he laughed at himself and refilled everyone's tea cups. "Are you all right, Grandpa?" asked his granddaughter. The question seemed to annoy the old man. "What do you think?" he snapped back at her. The purse snatcher was in his late teens or early twenties.

That year we celebrated Dr. Chen's eightieth birthday, although no one really knew how old he was. We rode our bicycles from Chengdu to his hometown in Pixian, some twenty-five to thirty kilometers away. That night returning home no one could keep up with the old man. By the time we got back, he was fast asleep. He offered just one word by way of explanation of how he was able to accomplish such feats: "*qì*."

Section Two: *Qì* and *Gōng Fū*

There is a simple phrase in Chinese that, like so many apparently simple Chinese sayings, contains a profound meaning. The phrase, *chī kŭ* 吃苦, literally means "eat bitter," that is, bear hardships. Figuratively, it serves as a standard that anyone who has ever practiced a martial art understands in the pit of their stomach. To "eat bitter" is the only way that one can develop *gōng fū*. What is *gōng fū*?

In yet another illustration of the way Westerners misunderstand and misinterpret things Chinese, the phrase *gōng fū* (or as it is more frequently written in the West, Kung Fu) is common to many forms of art and in many walks of life in China. *Gōng fū* 功夫 literally means "skill." The derivation of this word is worthy of a few sentences of explanation.

Gōng 功 is the same *gōng* we see in the phrase *qì gōng*. As explained earlier, it means exercise, particularly those kinds of exercise that require and/or develop artistic and athletic abilities. The word *fū* 夫 means "man" or "husband." The "sum" of the two words that make up the phrase *gōng fū* could be expressed in English as "man's exercise." There is a definite sexual or gender bias in this expression. It can be understood in a symbolic way, that is, the quality and quantity of work implied by *gōng fū* is symbolic of the ceaseless labor of men in the fields. The Chinese character for "man" is 男 *nán*. It is composed of two other characters. The upper portion is the character 田 *tián*, which means field. The lower portion is the character 力 *lì*, which means "strength" or "force." The force in the fields were men. Therefore, the considerable labor involved at earning survival from the fields stands as the symbol for the work that must be done to develop true skill. The routine, day-to-day, unending pattern of farm work, modulated as it is by the changing of the seasons along with the other rhythms of nature, describes the same sense of discipline.

There is another meaning of the word *gōng fū* in Chinese which relates in a vitally important way to this meaning. This meaning is "time." A more precise English word for what is meant here in the Chinese by "time" is "duration." The word *gōng fū* is used in expressions such as, "It only took him three days to learn to ice skate." The passage of time is expressed by *gōng fū*. In fact, in Chinese dictionaries this meaning of the word generally precedes others. Thus we can understand an important dimension of the meaning of the investment of labor required by traditional Chinese arts and disciplines to cultivate genuine skill. It cannot be done quickly. It must, by definition, take time. Another interpretation of *gōng fū* is contained in the old saying, "*gōng fū* is time and sweat."

Study and practice of the martial arts in China is understood to be a lifelong commitment. It is not so much a requirement as a simple observation of fact: without a lifetime's study and practice, true skill just does not develop. This is not to say that young people cannot and do not gain skills and benefits from the martial arts early; but rather that only those who devote themselves to long periods of study experience the ultimate achievements of these arts. With extraordinarily few exceptions, true masters of these arts are the old who have invested forty, fifty, or more years in daily practice. They are the ones with *gōng fū*. Another old saying goes, "*gōng fū* will not let down the man with a devoted heart."

Section Three: The External and the Internal

There are two primary "schools" of martial arts in China: external and internal. It is said that the external schools train the muscles, ligaments, and bones; while the internal schools train the *qì*. Not surprisingly, martial artists fight about almost everything; and there are certainly those who would contest this statement by arguing that the so-called external schools also include an intense concentration on developing internal strength or the power of the *qì*. Likewise, if pressed, adherents of the various internal disciplines would admit that the development of their techniques includes the strengthening of muscles, limbering of tendons, and cultivation of apparently external abilities.

What then is the actual distinction between these two approaches? Like so many issues related to traditional arts in China, it is not easy to grasp; the distinctions can seem imperceptibly subtle much of the time. In the final analysis, it is a highly personal matter. Most would agree or at least could accept that there is a difference in emphasis that characterizes these external and internal methods of cultivating and using the body's energies and forces.

In fact there are a series of characteristics that allow a general distinction among the internal and external schools of martial arts. The name "Internal School" or *nèi jiā quán* 内家拳 is applied to the three fighting arts of *tài jí, xíng yì,* and *bā guà*. This comes from events that occurred during the 1920s in Beijing. A group of boxers formed an alliance based on several factors they felt made it possible for students of one discipline to study with teachers of either of the other two, as if they were all of one family.

First, there is the matter of the mode of transmission of the teaching. These internal schools were traditionally developed and transmitted from father to son or otherwise through a private relationship between teacher and student. This included the student living inside the teacher's home. The teachings were retained as secrets within a particular family or tight-knit group. Thus, to study and acquire the techniques, one stayed inside the family home and structure.

On the other hand, the external schools were largely organized within temples and monasteries. Those who sought to learn disciplines such as *shào lín, é méi, bái hé,* and other boxing methods, were obliged to leave their family and travel to the temples where these arts were practiced and taught.

This might seem at first glance to be a superficial way to characterize the difference between two forms of the martial arts. But when the enormous importance of the family in traditional Chinese life is taken into account, this difference takes on a greater significance. Leaving his family is a profound step for a young Chinese boy. If he was leaving for a prolonged stay in a distant temple, such a step meant his life would develop in an altogether different way than if he had stayed at home. Finding a teacher outside the family, the student would address his new master as *shī fù* 師父, which literally means "teacher-father." This appellation implies that the devotion of the son has been transferred to the adopted teacher-father. Thus we should not underestimate the importance of differentiation between the internal and external schools.

A second important differentiation between the internal and external approaches to martial training and practice is the one referred to at the outset of this section. Indeed, the external schools do focus their training on the development of muscular strength, speed of movement, dexterity of the limbs, and coordination of the whole body. In general, they aim to harden the body's overall aspect to make it impervious to attack and irresistible by an opponent's defenses.

The internal schools stress the development of softness. They focus attention on the cultivation of mental, that is inward, methods of controlling *qì*, and rely upon this less tangible method to develop coordination and dexterity. Rather than feature muscular strength, they aim to develop the power of the *qì* through accumulating, refining, integrating, and focusing its potentials and motions.

Yet another distinction between the external and internal approaches to martial training lies in the selection of targets for attack. The external schools tend to focus their attack on the surfaces and externally visible portions of the opponent's body. That is, if the opponent attacks with his right hand, external schools block this attack and counter-attack against some part of the opponent's anatomy that has been left vulnerable.

On the contrary, the internal schools develop the ability to receive the opponent's attacking force, regardless of how it is delivered, and to return their force to the opponent. This returning force is either directed back in such a way as to uproot and discharge the opponent's whole body or it is focused at an internal organ. Here we see a particularly important distinction between the meaning of external and internal when applied to the martial arts.

A story that illustrates this distinction is told about the famous *tài jí* boxer, Yang Lu Chan. Yang's skill in fighting was legendary. Stories about this master are endless and all but impossible to verify. One possibly-apocryphal tale goes as follows. His reputation earned him an invitation to the Qing Court to join the emperor's personal bodyguard. Arriving to accept the appointment, Yang found himself the object of suspicion and jealousy on the part of the veteran guards. In fact, they conspired against him; and soon after he arrived, Yang was subjected to a vicious attack carried out one night by an assembly of the other guards. Setting upon him as a group, they beat and kicked him relentlessly as he lay sleeping in his bed. Leaving him for dead, they then returned to their respective rooms, content that they had, at the very least, taught the newcomer a stern lesson.

In the morning, however, the palace attendants learned a somewhat different lesson. Yang emerged stretching and yawning from his chamber. All of the other guards were found dead in their bunks, victims of severe internal injuries.

Another story that took place in the first half of the 20th century in this internal school illustrates a similar principle. Li Yu Lin, a long-time student of *xíng yì, bā guà,* and *tài jí* under the famous master Sun Lu Tang, was practicing Push Hands one day with his teacher. Li thought that as he was bigger and stronger than his teacher, he should be able to overcome him by sheer force. So thinking, he tried to release his strength against his teacher. To Li's surprise, Master Sun simply "neutralized" his ferocious push and continued as if nothing at all had happened. A few hours after they had finished their practice for the day, the student returned to his teacher. Li was sweating all over his body. His arms were bruised and aching. Sun addressed him sternly, "What were you thinking trying to hurt your teacher?" Li Yu Lin humbly apologized for his rudeness. Master Sun then informed him that he was suffering from internal injuries and gave Li some herbs to take. The next day, Li's arms were black; but thanks to his teacher's herbs, he recovered quickly.

Section Four: Masters and Secrets

Fighting for survival is a fact of life. A look into the traditions of virtually any culture anywhere on earth reveals long periods dominated by fighting and warfare. Indeed, history at times appears to be essentially a history of violent conflicts. Evidently, the skill and art of fighting and warfare plays an important part in the history of all humankind. This most definitely includes

Rubbing from a Han Dynasty tomb showing attacking warriors.

the history of the Chinese people. Among the most respected and widely studied manuals of fighting strategy and skill ever written is the ancient classic known in the West as the *Art of War (Sūn Zĭ Bīng Fă)* by Sun Zi from the Warring States period (475 B.C.E.–221 B.C.E.).

The roots of the fighting arts grow deep in Chinese history and culture. Like the fighting arts of many ancient civilizations, Chinese martial arts more than likely originated in the simple techniques developed by primitive people to defend themselves from their adversaries and to overpower their quarry. In this section we focus on the later, well-organized systems and methods of fighting, paying particular attention to the role of *qì* in the theories and practices that have developed over the past many centuries.

Among the earliest of such systematic organizations of martial techniques is contained in writings attributed to the sixth century Buddhist monk, Da Mo. He is more commonly known in the West by his Hindu name, Boddidharma, and by his position as the First Patriarch of Zen Buddhism. The word "Zen" is the Japanese pronunciation of a Chinese character, 禪 *chán*. This word, in turn, is a Chinese alliteration of a Hindu Buddhist term *dhyana*. The meaning of all three terms is the same: prolonged, intense contemplation.

Prolonged seated meditation or contemplation was a primary feature of the teaching of Boddidharma, who came to China in the sixth century, one of a number of Buddhist pilgrims who traveled back and forth between India and China for several centuries beginning in the first century C.E. According to Joseph Needham, there was extensive cross-fertilization of the cultures of these two great ancient nations during this period.[1]

The traditions of Buddhism were among the most profound of such Indian influences in China, and the teachings of Boddidharma galvanized the Buddhist community in China and have served as standard practices for Buddhists ever since.

[1] See Joseph Needham, *Science and Civilization in China,* Volume II.

Celebrated in folklore as well as official Buddhist scriptures, Boddidharma supposedly spent nine years in seated meditation in a cave before he himself achieved "awakening." This is the meaning of the phrase "prolonged seated meditation" in the previous paragraph. This typified the extraordinarily strenuous approach that he took to the practice of his religion. Perhaps, in part, as an antidote to such prolonged periods of sitting, he compiled a series of exercises designed to bend the limbs and stretch the sinews.

"Boddidharma [Da Mo] meditating in a cave," by Tai Chin. Liaoning Museum.

These bending and stretching exercises serve as the basis of a variety of martial arts and techniques developed in Buddhist temples throughout China. Of these, the most well-known outside of China is the *Shào Lín* 少林 Monastery in Henan Province. There, the monks devoted themselves to the teachings of the legendary Da Mo, which included a series of breathing techniques aimed at harnessing and developing a mysterious internal power. The nature of this mysterious power, though not easy to comprehend, is simple to name: it is the power of *qì*.

If Da Mo presents an incredible persona in the history of Chinese martial arts, it is even more difficult to distill fact from legend in the stories and songs that surround the life of Zhang San Feng, a Daoist monk from the Song Dynasty. Supposedly a resident of the Daoist temple located on Wu Dang mountain in Hubei province, Zhang San Feng is probably most well-known as the legendary creator of *tài jí quán*. In the forests beyond the monastery walls, he is believed to have observed the motions of animals

The legendary founder of *tái jí*, Zhang San Feng. Drawing from the Ming Dynasty text *Liè Xiān Quán Zhuàn.*

amid the forces of nature. Through diligence and meditation he connected his *qì* with the *qì* of nature, blended them ,and thereby made them excellent.

The oldest of the known classics of *tài jí quán* is attributed to Zhang San Feng, although like the other extant texts, it was transcribed in the nineteenth century by a famous boxer named Li Yi Yu from unverified sources. It contains vivid descriptions of the essence of the exercise along with concise expressions of its fundamental principles. It begins with lines that are well known to practitioners of *tài jí* around the world:

> *Once set in motion, the whole body is unified and must be light and filled with Spirit.*
>
> *(Yī jŭ dòng zhōu shēn jù yào qīng líng.)*

一舉動周身俱要輕靈

Zhang San Feng is credited with having written a variety of texts concerning the cultivation of *qì*, the preparation of the internal elixir, and the application of related principles to a sexual practice designed to facilitate *qì* cultivation. He was succeeded in this role of purveyor of the principles of *tài jí* by a series of martial artists with a literary bent. Foremost among these is Li Yi Yu who transcribed texts on *tài jí* in the latter part of the Qing Dynasty that have come to be revered as classics on the subject. Li attributed the authorship of these treatises to various great boxing masters of the past, according to Chinese custom. One of these supposed authors was Wang Zong Yue.

The opening of the *Wang Zong Yue Treatise on Tài Jí Quán* contains one of the most widely known phrases ever written on the subject.

Tài jí comes from wú jí
and is the Mother of yīn and yáng.
In motion it separates;
In stillness they fuse.[2]

The late professor Cheng Man Ching was a *tài jí* master of this tradition. He was one of the first *tài jí* practitioners to introduce the art widely in the United States. He settled in New York in the late 1950s and established a school of *tài jí* known as the School of Correct Timing where he taught until 1973. He returned to his home in Taiwan that year and died not long after. There are many interesting stories about the late professor.

Cheng Man Ching

One day he was introduced to a Daoist monk who had cultivated an extraordinary ability. This monk could make his body so light and control his balance so well that he could literally sleep suspended on a rope. He demonstrated this ability to Professor Cheng who responded enthusiastically.

"Please teach me how to do this wonderful and amazing feat," asked the Professor.

The monk knew of Professor Cheng's abilities in *tài jí quán* and replied, "Why waste your time learning to sleep on a string? You can be practicing *tài jí*!"

Chinese martial arts and *qì gōng* circles literally buzz with tales of amazing abilities and miraculous accomplishments. Several years ago we heard from a Swedish friend that one of his classmates from Stockholm had then recently become the first foreigner accepted into the training hall at the Shào Lín Monastery. What were the monks teaching him? To carry heavy weights suspended from his testicles. One of the old masters there could reportedly drag a 500-pound rock tied to his scrotum!

[2] Lo et al., *The Essence of T'ai Chi Ch'uan*, Berkeley. North Atlantic Books, 1985.

We're not sure what would be the purpose of such a skill. But we mention such things at the outset of this section to establish a perspective—to offer a few grains of salt with which the following material can be taken. This is not to suggest that all such stories are mere apocrypha.

Indeed, there was a lawsuit brought several years ago by a reporter in Hong Kong against the estate of the late abbot of the Shào Lín Monastery, Hai Deng. Hai Deng was a master of *shào lín* boxing and used to give public demonstrations of seemingly impossible feats which he and his students would perform. His trademark stunt was a one-finger "hand stand." He would literally hold up his entire body on one finger of one hand. He performed this skill publicly well into his seventies.

The reporter alleged in his suit that the oft-published photographs and accounts of Hai Deng's unique stunt were, in fact, phony. He sought relief from the courts for the fraud he contended the old master had perpetrated on the public. The court agreed to hear the suit, and when it had reviewed all the evidence issued its judgment. On the charge of fraud: Not Guilty. The reporter was ordered to pay all court costs. Hai Deng had been vindicated.

Section Five: *Tài Jí Quán, Qí,* and Their Relevance to Contemporary People

"The special quality of *tài jí quán*," according to the great twentieth century *tài jí* master, Cheng Man Ching, "is its ability to sink the *ch'i* to the *tan t'ien.*" For the past several decades, the art of *tài jí quán*, or "*yīn yáng* boxing" as it is sometimes called, has been rapidly and steadily growing in popularity outside of China. In fact, until the beginning of the 20th century, *tài jí* was a secret art within China. Given that *tài jí quán* has a history of several centuries at least (depending upon which story one accepts regarding its origins), it is only lately that its mysteries have been studied outside of a few families in China.

The system of postures and movements which was highly developed by the Chen clan in Hebei Province during the eighteenth and nineteenth centuries incorporated the fundamental principles of Daoist philosophy into a regimen of exercise, meditation, *qì gōng,* and martial techniques. The entire system depends upon a comprehension of *yīn* and *yáng*, for the name, *tài jí quán*, literally means "*tài jí* boxing." *Tài jí* 太極 is the term used to define the interrelationship of *yīn* and *yáng*. The well-known symbol of Daoism is known in Chinese as *tài jí tú* 太極圖, the diagram of *tài jí*. The word *tài jí* means "Greatest Limit."

Xiāng Yīn Xiāng Yáng

Tài jí quán is thus intimately linked with Daoist philosophy. The principles that flower in the classics of *tài jí* grow directly from Daoist roots. Thus in Chapter 40 of the *Dào Dé Jīng* we read, "*Dào* moves in cycles; *dào* functions through softness." In Chapter 43, we read, "Throughout heaven and earth, softness overcomes strength as a rider easily handles a galloping stallion. With nothingness you can enter where there is no door." In Chapter 76 we find, "At birth one is soft and supple, at death strong and hard." In Chapter 78, it is said, "Throughout the world nothing approaches the softness of water, but when it attacks anything strong, nothing can prevail against it. No one can change this. The soft overcomes the strong."

Practitioners of *tài jí quán* practice endowing their minds and bodies with such principles. The martial techniques are all based upon this strategy of the soft overcoming the hard. As we discussed in the foregoing section, this is one of the key differences between internal arts such as *tài jí* and the external schools of boxing.

In Chapter 48 of the *Dào Dé Jīng*, there is a puzzling admonition that says, "To follow the *dào*, you must lose everyday. Lose and lose again and again. Lose until you have nothing left to lose, until you attain non-action. Then, doing nothing, nothing remains undone." Professor Cheng had a saying that he often repeated to his students: "Invest in loss."

In such sayings we see the close connection between *tài jí quán* and the philosophy of the *dào*. Yet perhaps nowhere is the aim of Daoist cultivation more clearly stated than in one of the classical texts of *tài jí quán*: "Think over carefully what the final purpose is: to lengthen life and maintain youth." This simple sentence from an anonymous text, found in a salt shop in the nineteenth century, embodies the ancient dream of Daoists and guides millions of people around the world through their daily practice of *tài jí quán*.

But how does it work? There are many ways to approach the answer to this question. We know, through many years of study and practice of *tài jí*, that the only answers that matter are those that an individual develops for him- or herself. One of our *tài jí* teachers has a typical way of answering difficult questions about *tài jí*. A student asks, "Tell me teacher, how do we sink the *qì* to the *dān tián*?" Teacher replies, "Relax and practice." This same teacher sometimes has an even more blunt approach to dealing with students' troublesome questions. "Ask me in ten years' time. If you're still here practicing, then we can talk about it. And if you're not, then it doesn't matter anyway."

sōng (relaxation)

Clearly, the discipline of *tài jí* is one that takes a lifetime to comprehend. Yet people experience benefits from their study and practice from the first day they begin. As noted above, Professor Cheng Man Ching considered that the special feature of *tài jí quán* was its ability to sink the *qì* to the *dān tián*. When he was once asked if he had a secret which enabled him to maintain his level far beyond his students, he replied candidly, "There is a secret. I tell them every day, but it seems they don't believe me; or they don't take it seriously to heart. You have to relax the body and the mind completely."

There are indeed secrets to *tài jí quán*. As cannot be forgotten, the entire art was a well-guarded secret for generations until the beginning decades of the twentieth century when the late Yang Cheng Fu decided to teach his family's art widely. What are these secrets? Professor Cheng emphasized what is perhaps the simplest and most profound one. The secret of relaxation functions through a mechanism which, although not entirely secret, is not widely known or understood outside of *tài jí* circles. This mechanism is described in several lines from the classical texts of *tài jí*.

One of these classic lines states: "What is the proper use of the body? The mind commands; the muscles and bones obey." Another points out: "First it is in the mind; then it is in the body." One way to summarize this mysterious mechanism is to say that the *qì* follows the mind. This is the result of natural phenomena, the physiology and psychology of the human organism. Everyone has experienced this mechanism. In fact, its very real existence is verifiable through the most common of human experiences and emotions.

When we feel fear, for instance, the body responds with a recognizable series of responses. The fear need not be of any particular kind. We need not be confronted with clear and present physical danger or threat of immediate harm. For example, we can be talking on the telephone or reading a letter when we come face to face with a message that causes fear. The responses of the body and the mind in such instances, of course, tend to be less intense than in cases when we are threatened with clear and present danger. Yet even in the abstract circumstances of sitting alone and reading words on a piece of paper, we can undergo the dramatic physical changes that are characteristic of fear. Describing such phenomena in terms of *qì* and mind, we could say that the mental, emotional processes that we experience as fear guide the *qì* or functional energy of the body in characteristic ways that are designed to ready the body to respond to attack. We prepare to meet the agents in our environment that are the cause of our fear.

In fact, the ancient Chinese long ago described patterns of these characteristic responses of the body to the various emotions. For example: anger causes the *qì* to rise up; fright results in the sinking of the *qì*. Such awareness is not limited to practitioners of *tài jí quán*, but keeping in mind Professor Cheng's comment about the special quality of *tài jí,* we can begin to understand the meaning and function of relaxation in *tài jí* and its importance in accumulating and cultivating *qì*. By sinking the *qì* and the mind to the *dān tián,* they remain implicit, conserved for future cultivation or for use when extraordinary circumstances demand tapping these reserves.

Indeed, one of the ten important points that *tài jí* master Yang Cheng Fu included in his book on the subject was to "sink the *qì* to the *dān tián*." Recall that the *dān tián* 丹田 is a special point in the body, located approximately one and one-third inches below the navel in the interior of the body somewhat less than half way behind the front of the lower abdomen. Its

name reveals an important aspect of its significance. The word *dān* 丹 comes from Daoist alchemy. It is a name associated with the long-sought-after internal elixir [See Chapter 5]. The Daoists believed that an elixir of sorts could be fashioned without the use of herbs or chemicals through the concentration of *qì* 氣 and *jīng* 精 (essence) within the body. For various reasons, they settled on the spot they called *dān tián* as the ideal location within the body for the focus of this internal work. The word *tián* 田 means "field." Thus the *dān tián* is the "field of the internal elixir."

Tài jí quán, springing from Daoist sources, incorporates the *dān tián* as the focal point of the entire exercise. As Professor Cheng pointed out in the Afterword of *Cheng Tzu's Thirteen Treatises on T'ai Chi Ch'uan,* "First, the *tan t'ien* in *t'ai chi ch'uan* is the only path for the Taoist; there is no other way." Indeed, *tài jí* teachers who agree on little else can generally be found to be in accord on this one fundamental principle of the art: only by concentrating the *qì*, the functional power of the body, in the *dān tián* can the student make real progress.

Nuǎn Dān Tián, Warming the Dān Tián, from *Xiū Zhēn Mì Yào,* a Qing Dynasty text from 1506.

In the eleventh of his thirteen treatises on *tài jí quán,* Professor Cheng recorded the levels and degrees of *tài jí quán* through which a student should expect to progress over the course of a lifetime of study These were originally published in a book entitled *Cheng Tzu's Thirteen Treatises on T'ai Chi Ch'uan,* and were translated into English by Benjamin Lo and Martin Inn, both well-known teachers of *tài jí* in the United States and other countries. Here we quote the introductory paragraph to this treatise.

> *There are three different levels of T'ai Chi Ch'uan—Heaven, Earth, and Human. The Human Level relaxes your sinews and vitalizes your blood; Earth Level "opens the gates" so that the ch'i can reach the joints; and the Heaven Level exercises the sensory function. Each level has three degrees. The First Degree of the Human Level*

relaxes your tendons from the shoulders to the fingers. The Second Degree relaxes your tendons from the hip joint to the "bubbling well" [the first acupoint on the kidney channel located at the bottom of each foot]. The Third Degree relaxes your tendons from the sacrum to the top of the head (ní wán). The Earth Level First Degree sinks the ch'i to the tan t'ien. The Second Degree moves the ch'i into the bubbling well. The Third Degree circulates the ch'i so that it reaches the top of the head. The Heaven Level First Degree is t'ing chin [listening to intrinsic power]. The Second Degree is tung chin [understanding intrinsic power]. The Third Degree is omnipotence. These are the three levels and nine degrees.[3]

This section is not designed to be an instruction in *tài jí quán*. It is simply an attempt to reveal one important aspect of the art in the context of our broad discussion of *qì* and its importance in these many respects. *Tài jí* is a system of exercise, meditation, and martial techniques that develops many skills and results in substantial benefits for those who practice diligently over many, many years. But first and foremost it is a discipline for the accumulation, cultivation, and refinement of *qì*. This refinement can only be successfully conducted with a relaxed mind and body wherein the *qì* is directed and accumulated in the lower abdomen in that mysterious location known as the *dān tián*.

From Professor Cheng's introduction quoted above, it can be seen that even in the earliest stages of study and practice of *tài jí*, individuals can experience important benefits. The refinement of *qì* in the martial arts is not limited to the personal, individual scope. Just as philosophers, painters, poets, and doctors all contributed their special genius to the centuries-long development of the complex meaning of *qì*, so too have martial artists lent their unique view to the long-term accumulation of *qì*. In the words of one *tài jí* master:

Always keep something in reserve, something hidden which the opponent can neither see or know. In the classics it says, "The opponent doesn't know me. I, alone, know him." It also says, "Before the opponent's hands have touched the slightest hair on my arm, my mind has already penetrated his bones." Such skill can only be accomplished if

[3] As noted earlier, "*ch'i*" is an alternate romanization of the Chinese word *qì*, according to a system developed in the 19th century by two Englishmen named Wade and Giles. Throughout this book we use the contemporary romanization system of Chinese characters promulgated in the People's Republic of China in 1958 known as *Hàn Yǔ Pīn Yīn*, except in those instances where we quote from sources which use the earlier method of spelling. The Pinyin romanization of *ch'i* is *qì*.

you can remain quiet and hidden. If you want to be quiet and remain where the opponent cannot find you, you must keep your qì in reserve in the dān tián.

Both the metaphor and the concrete reality of the martial arts provide immediate and compelling expressions of the concept of *qì*. For centuries, philosophers and poets have sought the right word to contain the mysteries of *qì*. The painter who could capture *qì* and make it flow through paper and ink could bring to life a whole universe in a few strokes of the brush. The doctor who could observe the manifestations patients' *qì* and, through the use of herbs and needles rectify and harmonize its movements and transformations, could save lives. And the martial artist who can comprehend and cultivate the power of *qì* becomes a peerless boxer, one who "knows himself and knows his opponent and in one hundred battles gains victory one hundred times."

Perhaps the greatest manifestation of *qì*, however, is its influence on the daily lives of the Chinese people. Truly it is the thread from which the fabric of Chinese life is woven.

Chapter 7

Qì in Daily Life

Lin Yu Tang

"We do not know a nation until we know its pleasures of life," wrote Lin Yu Tang in his 1936 opus, *My Country, My People.* That we might better understand the pleasures of Chinese life, he also provided a list that illustrates the range of activities in which the Chinese engage, "given extensive leisure. ..."

> *They eat crabs, drink tea, taste spring water, sing operatic airs, fly kites, play shuttle-cock, match grass blades, make paper boxes, solve complicated wire puzzles, play mahjong, gamble and pawn clothing, stew ginseng, watch cock-fights, romp with their children, water flowers, plant vegetables, graft fruits, play chess, take baths, hold conversations, keep cage-birds, take afternoon naps, have three meals in one, guess fingers, play at palmistry, gossip about fox spirits, go to operas, beat drums and gongs, play the flute, practise on calligraphy, munch duck-gizzards, salt carrots, fondle walnuts, fly eagles, feed carrier pigeons, quarrel with their tailors, go on pilgrimages, visit temples, climb mountains, watch boat races, hold bull fights, take aphrodisiacs, smoke opium, gather at street corners, shout at aeroplanes, fulminate against the Japanese, wonder at the white people,*

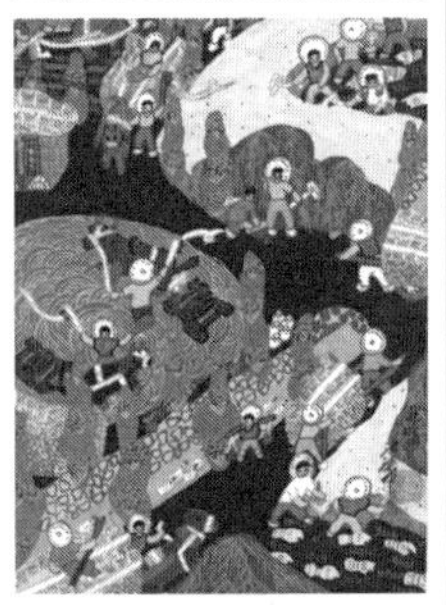

criticize their politicians, read Buddhist classics, practice deep-breathing, hold Buddhist séances, consult fortune tellers, catch crickets, eat melon seeds, gamble for moon cakes, hold lantern competitions, burn rare incense, eat noodles, solve literary riddles, train pot-flowers, send one another birthday presents, kow-tow to one another, produce children, and sleep.

As the poet Andrew Marvel lamented, had we but world enough and time, we could delineate the role of *qì* in each and every one of these activities. Moreover, *qì* is omnipresent in the Chinese concept of labor. Being with them in leisure and labor alike, the idea and the experience of *qì* thus lies at the very root of daily life in China.

Having explored historical aspects of the word *qì*, we turn now to this continuing presence in contemporary life. After all, a word which means so much about the vital energy of life should be expected to retain its own vitality. Indeed this is the case with *qì*. It runs through every aspect of life in China, appearing in expressions that foreigners learning the language and customs of the Chinese often find curious, even mysterious. But then, as we said at the outset, there is indeed something mysterious about *qì*.

SECTION ONE: *QÌ* IN MODERN CHINESE LANGUAGE

As we have suggested throughout the foregoing chapters, the word *qì* is a common household word in contemporary China. Walk down the streets of any Chinese city and you find it written on a variety of signs. Businesses engaged in a wide spectrum of enterprises announce their presence to the public through the use of this extraordinary word. The photo-montage on the facing page illustrates a few examples of such signage.

上海电气
二手
燃气炉
设备 饮料
紫氣東来
气球
标语
霓虹灯
广告接洽处
奔驰喇叭
轮胎·加气 补胎
检修汽车
国家医药局推荐药品
气管炎菌苗片
主治:急.慢性气管炎.支气管炎.哮喘.咳嗽.过敏性鼻炎等呼吸道系统疾病
尤适于流感流行期的老人和儿童患者
中国济南·齐鲁制药厂

Sequence of the changes in the writing of the character *qì*

The following is a list of common Chinese expressions containing the word *qì*. We have included some words and phrases in which the word appears in a variant form, 汽, which is pronounced the same as *qì* 氣 and which means "vapor" or "steam." The difference between these two Chinese characters is the addition of the water radical to *qì*. When water 水 is added to other characters on the left hand side, it appears as 氵. In this case, this implies *qì* 气 and water mixed together, i.e., steam or vapor.

To be prudent, we must explain the sudden change of the appearance of the character *qì* from 气 to 氣. For this purpose we need to refer back to Section One of Chapter 1 where we discuss the etymology of the word *qì*. As shown, one of its original meanings was "the mist which rises and forms the clouds." Its roots in ethereal concepts give rise to its changing forms and extended meanings over time. It was a pictorial graph of this natural phenomenon. In fact, these are two separate words in Chinese; but the sense is similar enough, we believe, to justify inclusion of such words in the list below. The purpose of this list is to illustrate the wide range of usages that are animated by the concept of *qì*.

Ào qì 傲氣: air of arrogance, haughtiness.

Biē qì 憋氣: feel suffocated or oppressed; choke with resentment, feel injured and resentful.

Bù yòng kè qì 不用客氣 or ***bù bì kè qì*** 不必客氣: you're welcome (literally, "don't use a guest's airs," i.e., "don't be polite," i.e., "don't mention it").

Chà qì 岔氣: feel a pain in the chest when breathing.

Chū qì 出氣: give vent to one's anger; vent one's spleen.

Chū qì kǒu 出氣口: gas outlet; air vent.

Dà qì 大氣: the atmosphere.

Gǔ qì 骨氣: strength of character; moral integrity; backbone.

Fèi qì 廢氣: waste gas or steam.

Fēng qì 風氣: general mood, atmosphere; common.

Fú qì 福氣: happy lot, good fortune.

Fù qì 負氣: do something in a fit of pique.

Hé qì 合氣: to engage in sexual intercourse (literally, "unite the *qì*").

Hé qì 和氣: gentle, kind, polite, good-natured.

Huǎn qì 緩氣: get some breathing room, have a respite, take a breather.

Huì qì 晦氣: unlucky.

Huǒ qì 火氣: anger, temper; in Chinese medicine: internal heat.

Jiā qì 加氣: speed it up, i.e., "step on the gas;" to buy gasoline.

Jiāo qì 嬌氣: fragile, delicate; squeamish; finicky.

Jié qì 節氣: in the Chinese lunar calendar, a day marking one of the twenty-four divisions of the solar year, i.e., one of the solar terms.

Jiě qì 解氣: vent one's spleen, work off one's anger.

Kè qì 客氣: manners, politeness.

Kǒu qì 口氣: tone, note; manner of speaking; implication.

Méi qì 没氣: to feel strengthless; to be dead.

Míng qì 名氣: reputation, fame, name.

Nuǎn qì 暖氣: central heating.

Pēn qì 噴氣: jet propelled.

Pí qì 脾氣: temperament, disposition; bad temper.

Qì chē 汽車: automobile.

Qì bèng 氣泵: air pump.

Qì fēn 氣氛: atmosphere.

Qì gēn 氣根: aerial root.

Qì huà 氣化: gasification.

Qì jié 氣節: integrity; moral courage.

Qì jiǔ 氣酒: sparkling wine.

Qì làng 氣浪: blast (of an explosion).

Qì lì 氣力: effort, energy, strength.

Qì liàng 氣量: tolerance.

Qì nǎo 氣惱: anger, vexation.

Qì pài 氣派: manner, style, air.

Qì pò 氣魄: moral strength, breadth of spirit.

Qì qiú 氣球: balloon (literally, "*qì* ball").

Qì sè 氣色: complexion, color (of the face or skin).

Qì shì 氣勢: momentum; imposing manner.

Qì sǐ 氣死: to make (someone) angry.

Qì tǐ 氣體: gas.

Qì tūn shān hé 氣吞山河: spirit that can conquer mountains and rivers.

Qì wèi 氣味: smell, odor, flavor.

Qì xī 氣息: breath; flavor; smell.

Qì xiàng xué 氣象學: meteorology.

Qì xū xū 氣吁吁: gasping, panting for breath.

Qì yā 氣壓: atmospheric pressure, barometric pressure.

Qì yóu 汽油: gasoline.

Qì zhí 氣質: temperament, disposition.

Sàng qì 喪氣: feel disheartened, lose heart, become crestfallen.

Shā qì 殺氣: murderous look; vent one's ill feelings.

Shàn qì 疝氣: hernia, rupture.

Shàng qì bù jiē xià qì 上氣不接下氣: be out of breath, gasp for breath.

Shén qì 神氣: expression, air, manner; spirited, vigorous; putting on airs, cocky.

Shēng qì 聲氣: information; voice, tone.

Shēng qì 生氣: to get angry (literally, to make *qì*); vitality, life.

Shèng qì líng rén 盛氣凌人: domineering; arrogant; overbearing.

Shī qì 濕氣: moisture, dampness; eczema, fungal infection of hands or feet.

Shì qì 士氣: morale.

Shǒu qì 手氣: luck at gambling, card playing, etc.

Shòu qì 受氣: be bullied.

Shū shēng qì 書生氣: bookishness.

Sōng qì 松氣: relax one's efforts.

Sú qì 俗氣: vulgar; in poor taste.

Tāi qì 胎氣: nausea, vomiting, and edema of the legs during pregnancy.

Tàn qì 嘆氣: sigh, heave a sigh.

Tiān qì 天氣: weather.

Tōng qì 通氣: ventilate; aerate; be in touch, keep each other informed.

Xí qì 習氣: bad habit, bad practice.

Xǐ qì yáng yáng 喜氣洋洋: full of joy, jubilant.

Xiāo qì 消氣: cool down; become mollified.

Xiǎo qì 小氣: stingy, niggardly, mean; narrow minded, petty.

Xiào qì 笑氣: laughing gas, nitrous oxide.

Xié qì 邪氣: perverse trend; evil influence.

Xiè qì 泄氣: lose heart, feel discouraged; disappointing, frustrating; pathetic.

Xīn píng qì hé 心平氣和: even tempered and good humored; calm.

Xiù qì 秀氣: delicate, elegant, fine; (of manners) refined, urbane; well-made.

Yáng méi tǔ qì 揚眉吐氣: blow off steam in rejoicing.

Yáng qì 洋氣: foreign flavor; Western style; outlandish ways.

Yī qì 一氣: at one go, without a break; of the same gang; a spell or fit.

Yì qì 意氣: will and spirit; temperament; personal feelings.

Yǒng qì 勇氣: courage, nerve.

Yǔ qì 語氣: tone, manner of speaking; mood.

Yuán qì 元氣: vitality, vigor.

Yuàn qì 怨氣: grievance, complaint; resentment.

Yùn qì 運氣: fortune, luck.

Zhāo qì 朝氣: youthful spirit, vigor, vitality.

Zhèng qì 正氣: healthy atmosphere (or tendency); vital energy.

Zhì qì 志氣: aspiration; ambition.

Why have we listed out all these words? This list could be easily extended to two or three times its length. If you listen and watch for it carefully, you find the word *qì* appearing with great frequency in the Chinese language. But of what meaning is this fact? Does it imply that all Chinese are philosophers, cosmologists, Daoists searching for the internal elixir, or practitioners of *qì gōng* or *tài jí quán?*

Certainly not. In fact, the great majority of Chinese people would probably tell you they have no understanding at all of these esoteric aspects of their culture. But does that mean that they are not influenced by the presence of such concepts in the cultural matrix from which they were born and in which they exist? What can we know about China and her people from this examination of *qì* in daily life? What does the presence of *qì* in Chinese life and language really mean?

We posed such question to many of our teachers, colleagues, students, and friends in China looking for a range of opinions and answers. What we gained is an understanding of the fact that the concept of *qì* is virtually inseparable from the concept of life itself in the minds of Chinese people. Whether it is foremost in their thoughts and actions, as in the case of those who rise early every morning and practice various forms of exercise and meditation to cultivate and accumulate their *qì*, or whether it merely exists as a subliminal influence of the words they think and speak, *qì* gives the Chinese life. For when they lose their *qì*, their life is over.

To understand how and why this one word functions in this fundamentally important way, we examine several of the common experiences and expressions of *qì* more closely.

Section Two: Familiar Experiences and Expressions of *Qì*

If we examine the preceding list of ninety-four words and phrases containing the character *qì* 氣, several interesting observations about the word begin to emerge. First, these words can be organized into three categories: words that deal with atmospheric conditions and other natural phenomena such as gas, steam, etc.; words that express some aspect of a person's emotional or internal state; and words that deal with the interpersonal or social milieu. However, in each of these categories the word *qì* supplies the sense of movement, flow, connectivity, or information.

As an example, take the word *shén qì* 神氣. We have seen this word many times in the foregoing chapters, where we discussed it in terms of its ancient, philosophical, or medical meanings. But this word has a common meaning in modern Chinese. Like its ancient and specialized meanings, this common meaning emerges quite readily from a consideration of its two component characters. *Shén* 神, once again, means spirit, god, divinity, supernatural, magical, expression, appearance (used especially of the face), smart, or clever. Joined together with the word *qì*, the meaning becomes "expression," "air," or "manner." It might appear in a sentence in Chinese having the meaning: "He had an air of complacency about him," or "His manner of speaking is very much like his father's."

Shén qì also means vigorous, spirited. It could be used in a sentence expressing the idea that "She looks so full of spirit in her new outfit." *Shén qì* also means "putting on airs" or "cocky." It can be used to express an idea such as, "What makes you think you're so great?" In each of these uses, *qì* lends its motive force to the concept of *shén*. It emphasizes the movement of the spirit, that is, its manifestation and appearance. This reflects that aspect of the most ancient meaning of *qì* mentioned at the beginning of Chapter 1: *qì* is often invisible, but through its changes it can be sensed and experienced.

Another word from the list in Section One, above, illustrates another characteristic of *qì* that commonly manifests in Chinese language, thought, and experience. The word *tōng qì* 通氣 has two meanings that can appear quite unrelated at first glance. The first is "to ventilate or aerate." The second is "to stay in touch with one another" or "to keep one another informed." A look at the combined significance of these two characters *tōng* 通 and *qì* 氣 reveals the underlying relationship between these two apparently disparate meanings.

Tōng means "connect," "open (as of a road)," "thorough" (as in the word thoroughfare), "communicate," "lead to," "go to," "notify," "understand," "know," "authority," "expert," "logical," "coherent," "general," "common," "all," and "whole." Air is one of the most common meanings of *qì*; and it is quite easy to understand how "connect air" comes to mean "ventilate." As we have mentioned many times throughout this book, one of the primary functions of the concept of *qì* is providing connectivity to whatever usage it is employed. However, the expression "*tōng qì*" can be understood to mean "communicate and connect" or, as explained above, "to stay in touch" or "keep one another informed." This raises a question as to how *qì* comes to mean "communication."

In fact, what is revealed in an expression like *tōng qì* is a broad metaphoric basis of one of the more subtle yet important meanings of *qì*: information. Nowhere is this meaning more clearly seen than in Chinese medicine. *Qì* is the substance that connects the entire organism of the human body together through the system of circulatory pathways known in Chinese medicine as *jīng luò*. Another way of expressing this same idea is to say that the *qì* of the body is the medium for the exchange of information between any one part or function of the body and all others. This same metaphor can be seen in terms of the genetic code, DNA. The DNA molecule can be understood as a densely packed information storage and transmission system. From the genetic information of the combined DNA of mother and father, a whole new life emerges through an amazingly complex pattern of replication and reproduction of instructions, i.e., highly specialized information. In Chinese medicine, this informational dimension of the human experience is expressed in the concept of the *jīng qì* or the *qì* of the essence. One way to understand the difference between the words *jīng* 精 and *jīng qì* 精氣 is that the former emphasizes the substantial aspect of this genetic essence whereas the latter implies its functional aspect or its manifestation. Once again, it is through the transformative and connective function of *qì* that we can become aware of the presence of otherwise strictly implicit and invisible potentials and substances.

This abstract metaphor which finds *qì* serving as the information medium of the human body is rooted in ancient philosophical concepts. It developed the unique and comprehensive description of human anatomy and physiology over the centuries of its use as a term in Chinese medicine, and it expresses itself in the phrase, "*tōng qì*," or as we would say in English, "Stay in touch."

As we discussed in Chapter 4, traditional Chinese medicine is an ancient storehouse of wisdom concerning relationships between the body's various structures and functions. This includes important emotional dimensions of understanding. Doctors of Chinese medicine have known for thousands of years that emotional disturbances, as well as long-term unwanted emotional states, can disturb the natural movements of *qì* throughout the body. This often results in a variety of illnesses. The medical understanding has pervaded Chinese culture in many ways. To illustrate this point, we can examine the concept and experience of anger.

The eighth definition of *qì* in the *Great Dictionary of Chinese Characters (Hàn Yŭ Dà Zì Diăn),* as listed in Chapter 1, is "anger." Like many Chinese words, *qì* can be used as a noun, a verb, or a modifier. In modern Chinese there is a common phrase that includes the word *qì* that conveys the meaning of the verb "to anger," "to make angry," or "to become angry." *Shēng qì* 生氣 literally means "give birth (or give rise) to *qì*." Provoking someone (or being provoked) to anger is thus expressed as the process of generating

qì. Here we see a typically pragmatic Chinese awareness that anger animates the organism and prepares it for increased activity. Thus in the red faces and bulging eyes of the angry, the Chinese see a common manifestation of *qì*. Again, this manifestation is thoroughly explained in traditional Chinese medical theory. When the *qì* of the liver is unrestrained (as in conditions in which the substance or *yīn* of the liver is compromised or damaged through disease, injury, alcohol, or emotional influences), it rises upward, like a wind inside the person. To a doctor of Chinese medicine, the red eyes of anger are a symptom of the *yáng qì* of the liver that is unrestrained by the *yīn* substance of the liver, thus rising uncontrollably to manifest in the sense organ (the eye) to which the liver opens.

How bad can it get? Look at the expression, "*qì sǐ wǒ* 氣死我!" It translates into English as "That really ticks me off!" Or worse, of course, depending on the tone of voice. The literal meaning? "*Qì* me to death." In Chinese medicine, the same metaphor extends to the life threatening implications of the *qì* of the liver rising uncontrollably as internal wind, for this is the traditional explanation of the etiology of "wind stroke" (*zhòng fēng* 中風) or apoplexy.

Qì is a powerful force and factor of life in China. It is woven throughout the language. Another example of the omnipresence of *qì* in Chinese life is one that is not just heard all over the country every single day, it is broadcast on TV. Virtually every news broadcast in China, like news broadcasts all around the world, include a weather report. On Chinese TV programs, the weatherman or weatherwoman gives the "*tiān qì bào dào* 天氣報道," the report of the *qì* of the heavens—the weather report. The word *tiān* 天 means "heaven" and "sky." Throughout this book, this is the Chinese word that appears over and over in the ancient literature about the "*qì* of heaven and earth."

In modern Chinese, the *qì* of heaven, *tiān qì* 天氣, means "weather." Meteorology, the science of the weather, is *qì xiàng* 氣象, literally, "the appearance of the *qì*." The air that Chinese people breathe is *kōng qì* 空氣, literally, "empty *qì*." There simply is no more common experience than breathing. This is what we mean when we say that *qì* is a common experience in Chinese life. The atmosphere itself is understood to be "the big *qì*" (*dà qì*) 大氣.

What is the point of all this? What are driving toward?

This book is the result of various things. We have been studying, practicing, and trying to come to terms with a number of traditional Chinese arts and sciences for many years. Throughout the entire time, one of the most common experiences we have had is asking or being asked, "What is *qì*?" A fairly typical if somewhat insensitive answer such a question frequently elicits from Chinese individuals is, "*Qì* is *qì*."

Perhaps this is not such an insensitive answer after all. For the Chinese, who experience *qì* literally in every breath they take, it may well be enough to know that *qì* is *qì*. But for those who come from other cultural backgrounds, hearing that *qì* is *qì* means next to nothing. The problem is that once we begin to dig into the matter, once we roll up our sleeves and investigate what *qì* really is, it is hard to stop.

Qì is such an integral part of the experience of life and language in China that it can seem almost impossible to pull this one thread out of the embroidery of Chinese culture without entirely unraveling it. What we've experienced far too often in the past is that those who start to tug on it will pull too quickly and the will thread break. Or they will give up and never find how far it winds through the fabric of Chinese thought. Perhaps worst of all, they succeed at freeing a small fragment of the thread of *qì* from the complex brocade of its multi-dimensional meanings and are left with a paltry impression of how *qì* functions to connect so much that is vital and thriving in the Chinese cultural imagination.

That is why we wrote this book. For many years we have argued with students, teachers, colleagues, friends, and family that to understand and express anything like the full range of meanings of this one Chinese word, we would have to write a whole book. Perhaps all we have done is to construct a self-fulfilling prophecy. But if we have managed to convey something of the breadth and depth which the word *qì* spans, then the time and effort of both we, the writers, and you, the reader, have been well spent.

We are not finished yet.

Section Three: Qì and the Chinese Worldview

We have suggested that the concept of *qì* pervades and connects all aspects of Chinese cultural life. We have presented evidence of *qì's* ancient past as well as its widespread presence in contemporary life and language in the Chinese speaking world. We turn now to an examination of the Chinese worldview in order to begin to bring our brief history of *qì* to a close.

What is a worldview? Does a country have a worldview? Do you have a worldview? What do we mean, as simply as possible, by the phrase "the Chinese worldview?"

We think of a worldview as a characteristic pattern of habits of perception and interpretation of phenomena and events that are the common property of a majority of Chinese people. Here we must keep in mind that although the People's Republic of China comprises some fifty-six nationalities, that is to say, ethnic and/or racial groups, the vast majority of the Chinese population belong to just one of these groups, the Han. The Han account for some ninety-five percent of China's 1.2 billion people. What we mean by "the Chinese worldview" is largely limited to those characters of perception and interpretation that are either genetically transmitted or that are learned within the family and/or extended family structures. To be precise, what we will discuss is the Han Chinese worldview. This could alternately be described as the ways in which the Han have taught their children to look at and comprehend what life is about, generation after generation, for thousands of years.

One of the aspects of the Chinese worldview that gives it a unique character is the length of its span through time. The Chinese conceive of themselves as a people with an ancient cultural heritage. One of the primary factors that connects contemporary Chinese with this ancient legacy of ideas and experiences is *qì*. Thus the connectivity of *qì* manifests in the temporal as well as spatial dimensions of Chinese life. It connects all aspects of life in China into an integrated whole.

Chapter 25 of the *Dào Dé Jīng* contains one of the book's most famous passages:

> *There are four great phenomena in this universe. Humankind is one of these. Humankind follows the earth. The earth follows heaven. Heaven follows Dào. The Dào follows nature.*

Humankind is thus positioned in this vast scheme of the movements of nature. Yet, the traditional Chinese outlook also reflects what is frequently characterized as Daoist mystical skepticism as is reflected in another passage from Chapter 23 of the *Dào Dé Jīng*.

> *It is the way of nature to express but little. Hurricanes do not last a whole morning. Thunderstorms cannot last all day. What causes these? Heaven and earth. If even heaven and earth are unable to persevere for long periods, then how can mankind last much longer?*

The concept of humankind's harmonious integration with nature is a fundamental aspect of the Chinese worldview. We saw an example of how deeply the integration of humans and nature is ingrained when we saw how it is a critically important aspect of traditional Chinese medical theory. Just as the conception of *qì* connects the Chinese of today with their ancient ancestors, so too do the various phenomena named by *qì* connect the parts and functions of the body into an organic whole. The entire concept of disease in this traditional context is predicated upon the notion that disharmonies in the various bodily relationships to which humans are subject develop as a result of the movements and exchanges of *qì*. Such disharmonies are primarily considered in terms of the relationships between man and nature. But they include disharmonies between individuals as well as disharmonies that arise within an individual. These are all reflections of the Chinese view of life.

In this context, given that we aimed at illuminating this subject for Western readers, we turn to a Western frame of reference to find common ground from which to construct a bridgework across the considerable cultural gap that exists between China and the West. In surveying modern civilization for a place to begin the Western end of our cultural bridge, the work of Sigmund Freud comes rapidly to mind. It is hard to find any body of work that exceeds Freud's in terms of its influence on how contemporary Westerners look at themselves and the world. Naturally, there have been other great influences during the past two hundred years, but for our purposes, understood as a sample and not as unique, Freud will do.

To begin, Freud's work is synonymous with sexuality. Freud's theory of the libido, or inborn urge towards sexual satisfaction, is a primary ingredient of his understanding of the mind. It is the mind, after all, that engages in the perception that results in a worldview. Therefore, the concept of "mind" that people hold to be true is of enormous importance in understanding how they look at their world. Freud's concept of mind occupies an enormously important position in Westerner's self-image. Indeed, the modern concepts of the "self" or "ego" are direct results of Freud's writings.

Leaving aside for now the complexities of mental structure and function contained in Freud's work, we can focus on the subject of sexuality. As it is the means by which humans procreate, it is unquestionably of fundamental importance in life and therefore in one's view of life. The sexual act is described in a virtually infinite variety of ways in languages around the world. People everywhere talk about sex all the time—whether in beer halls, locker rooms, or over tea and dim sum. And there is much that can be understood about people by listening to what they say about sex.

If we listen to Chinese people talk about sex, as indeed they do (contrary to erroneous Western stereotypes of the shy Oriental), we hear phrases that reveal once again the presence of the concept of *qì*. We listed one such phrase above on page 165, *hé qì* 合 氣. This is an intimate expression used by lovers in China for the act of lovemaking. Literally it means, "the union of *qì*" or "join *qì*." Naturally, there are countless other expressions for the sexual act in Chinese. But this one expression reveals that in this fundamentally important act of sexual intercourse, the Chinese see themselves joining their *qì* with the *qì* of their partner.

If we accept the Freudian precept that sexuality is indeed a fundamental motive force underlying all mental processes, then the role of *qì* in the Chinese worldview has been defined by lovers throughout China as a fundamental and central one. We take it for granted that such an awareness may lie beneath the level of consciousness of a vast majority of Chinese people, regardless of whether or not they have ever spoken or heard the phrase, "*hé qì*." This only serves to bring the role of *qì* into closer alignment with the Freudian perspective. For in Freudian terms, the role of sexuality itself is often buried deep below the level of conscious thinking, yet we experience its influence and see its manifestations emerge with or without conscious awareness.

We need not look so deep, however, to see reflections of *qì* in the eyes and minds of Chinese people as they gaze across the landscapes and down the streets and by-ways of their daily lives. The Chinese see *qì* everywhere. It's in the air they breathe. It is the force that drives the fusion of their blood. They take it from the food they eat. They add it to their cars to make them run. They burn it to eat and stay warm in their homes. They feel it in the winds of thought that blow through their minds. And, when they follow the deepest urges of their hearts, they join their *qì* with the *qì* of their lovers. *Qì* gives them life, and when they lose their *qì*, they die.

The function of *qì* is to pervade and connect the micro- and macro- systems that comprise the totality of existence. It is the medium as well as the motive force of universal communications. This is a communication that precedes language, precedes thought. It is the Prime Force that first appeared when the universe was born. It arises from the interplay of *yīn* and *yáng*. It binds these two most essential aspects of existence together into the unity of the universe; these two polar potentials produce the *qì* of all creation.

A final note on the subject of the Chinese way of looking at the world: the traditional Chinese worldview focuses on the center. The word in Chinese for center is *zhōng* 中. Its ancient form is a pictograph of a flag staff with signal flags flying in the wind, . These ancient flags were the medium of battlefield communications and command. Thus the word *zhōng* contains echoes of China's turbulent military past in which the national identity was forged on the field of battle. The modern character has clearly developed into a glyph that pictorially represents the notion of centrality, the vertical piercing the center.

Zhōng symbolizes the national identity of China. The name of China in Chinese is *Zhōng Guó* 中國, the Central Country. As we saw in Chapter 5 and 6, the concept of the center is of unparalleled importance in the various practices and disciplines that have flourished for thousands of years in China for the purpose of accumulating, cultivating, and refining of *qì*. The center of the human anatomy is the location called *dān tián*.

Dì Sān Shé Jiǎo Shù Yān Tú, The Third Mingling of the Tongue, Gurgling and Swallowing Diagram. From the book, *Bā Duàn Jǐn Zuò Lì Gōng (Eight Pieces of Brocade Sitting and Standing Practices)*, an 1875 Qing Dynasty text by Lie Jie.

It is the field of the internal elixir where the ultimate magic of the Daoist is performed. Thus in the Chinese name for China we can see a subtle and profound association between these ancient concepts and the national identity. The center is the place where the *qì* accumulates. For the Chinese people throughout their long history, China itself is this center in which the *qì* of heaven and earth has been accumulating since time began. This accumulation of *qì* since time immemorial has congealed the spirit of the Chinese nation. It moves wherever Chinese people and their traditions go. For several centuries it has traveled beyond its native China to fill the imaginations of Westerners who find its mysterious power attractive. Today more than ever, we witness *qì* gathering throughout the world.

Section Four: The Future of *Qì*

Given its long and complex history, it would be odd to think of the notion of *qì* as an idea whose time has come. Yet we neglect an important aspect of the discussion of the history of *qì* if we ignore the implications of this idea for the future. We have already touched upon several of these implications. Let us now address them directly.

In the Fall of 2000, as we were working to finalize the manuscript of this book, we experienced a curious bit of synchronicity. It seems like a perfect way to bring this brief history to a close. Here's what happened.

One afternoon a friend, Larry Karush, whose brilliance as a composer and pianist was recognized in 2000 with the award of a grant from the Guggenheim Foundation, was telling us about his upcoming residency at the Wurlitzer Foundation in Taos, New Mexico. As he was leaving, we had a conversation that went something like this:

"Larry, when you're in New Mexico, keep in mind that we'd love to find a contact at the Santa Fe Institute, someone there who might be interested in exploring the implications of *qì* in complexity and chaos theory."

"Yeah," said Larry with a grin. "Sure. I'll keep it in mind."

Admittedly, it was a far-fetched idea. Larry wasn't even going to Santa Fe. But scarcely a week later, we got a phone call from Dr. Thomas Kepler, the Vice President of Academic Affairs at the Santa Fe Institute.

"If you have a minute, I'd like to talk to you about Chinese medicine," began Tom. And during the course of our conversation, he told this story.

"Just the other day, a woman stuck her head in my office and asked me, 'Are you the guy around here who does Chinese medicine?' I told her no but asked her to come in and explain why she'd even think to ask me that."

The woman, Judy Strasser, was a Poet-in-Residence at the Wurlitzer Foundation up the road in Taos where she'd just met our friend, Larry.

They'd got to talking, and when Judy told Larry she was going to Santa Fe to take part in a conference at the Santa Fe Institute, Larry recalled our conversation.

"See if you can find out who's doing Chinese medicine there," said Larry.

So she did.

As it turns out, the Institute had recently received a grant to support a program to disseminate SFI-style research in China, India, and the former Soviet Union. Tom Kepler had gotten the assignment of developing projects to implement this program. He considered Chinese medicine, reasoning that it might just provide a suitable subject area into which the SFI approach to research could be introduced to Chinese scientists. He also thought that the Institute might be able to help develop effective methods for Western scientists to comprehend the similarities and differences between modern medicine and traditional Chinese medicine.

He was very interested, to say the least, when this woman stuck her head in his office and asked him if he was the guy doing Chinese medicine. As we talked, he grew more interested to learn that we had written a book exploring the cultural roots of medicine in China, *Who Can Ride the Dragon?* After a half an hour on the phone, he invited us to Santa Fe to talk about his plans.

In November we met with Tom and others at SFI and began what promises to be a long and fascinating series of conversations devoted to further exploration into how to bridge the gaps that exist between Chinese doctors and researchers and their Western counterparts who are interested in bringing the wisdom and benefits of this ancient healing art into use in the 21st century.

In Chapter 2 we examined the role of Chinese ideas in the development of Western scientific thinking, admittedly in a superficial fashion. There is, however, a deep vein through which essential artifacts of Chinese thought have flowed into the consciousness and culture of the Western world.

Consider two such artifacts: gunpowder and the magnetic compass. Both of these originated in China. Moreover, each can be seen to have profound connections with that body of philosophical material at the center of which we find the notion of *qì*.

The formula for gunpowder was discovered by Daoist alchemists in search of the elixir of life. In fact, according to Joseph Needham, the invention of gun powder traces back specifically to Sun Si Miao, one of the most renowned doctors in Chinese history.[1]

[1] Joseph Needham, *Science and Civilization in China*, Vol 2, Cambridge. Oxford University Press, 1956.

In the Tang Dynasty (618 C.E–906 C.E.), he stumbled on this potent blend of chemicals in search and refinement of an elixir of immortality. According to their extensive and elaborate theories, that blend of ingredients possessed the proper blend of qualities to engender the fabled *dān* or elixir of immortality.

What qualities? In essence, these qualities were all understood and measured in terms of *yīn* and *yáng*; and as we have made clear, whenever we speak of *yīn* and *yáng* we speak, if only by implication, of *qì*. In short, the Daoist experimenters who went looking for a formula that would harmonize their *yīn* and *yáng*, i.e., that would connect their *qì* to the *qì* of nature and enable them to nourish themselves on the endless flow of universal *qì*, wound up producing the mixture of molecules that result in gunpowder. This is, perhaps, one of the great ironies of the history of human science, given that this invention of these dedicated Daoists has been used principally as an instrument of killing and destruction. Awareness of such ironies, however, should not make us any the less sensitive to the fact that the epochal influence of gunpowder on Western civilization stems from Chinese sources.

The magnetic compass represents another manifestation of the theory of *yīn* and *yáng* that arrived on Western European shores with epochal results. What is particularly interesting is the fact that what guided the early Chinese to discover the magnetic polarity of the earth was very likely, according to Joseph Needham, the philosophy of the *dào*, i.e., of *yīn* and *yáng* and of *qì*.

> *Chinese were familiar with the south-pointing properties of pieces of magnetite made into short spoons and capable of turning about the axis of their bowls. One is at liberty to wonder whether it was only a coincidence that in a world where everything was connected with everything else, according to definite correlative rules, it should have occurred to the magician-experimenters as natural or possible that a piece of lodestone carved into the shape of the Northern Dipper should partake of its cosmic directivity? In a way, the whole idea of the Tao was the idea of a field of force. All things oriented themselves according to it, without having to be instructed to do so, and without the application of mechanical compulsion. The same idea springs to the mind, as will shortly be seen, in connection with the hexagrams of the I Ching, Yang and Yin, Chhien and Khun, acting as the positive and negative poles respectively of a cosmic field of force. Is it so surprising, therefore, that*

it should have been in China that men stumbled upon what was in very deed the field of force of their own planet?

It was just such considerations of the influence that the concept of *qì* has exerted directly and indirectly on the progress of human knowledge that led us to want to establish contact with the Santa Fe Institute. Over the past several centuries, scientists, writers, engineers, and thinkers of all kinds in the West have made enormous use of *qì* and the various artifacts that have grown up in its sphere.

Is it possible that hidden among the treasures that the West has imported from China over the past several centuries there lies an essential element of human knowledge that might be of use to those engaged in the search for a new synthesis of scientific understanding of the world in which we live? People turn to the past in greater numbers day by day to find some kernel of wisdom to guide them through the grand mess of real life.

If such a find is to be made, if such an artifact of human thought yet remains to be discovered and brought into the service of modern people, we will have to answer a question that was put to us quite directly by Tom Kepler in November, 2000.

Walking on the footpath that winds its way around the main building at the Santa Fe Institute, we looked out across the city of Santa Fe, the plateau where it lies and the mountain peaks that rise from the Western horizon and stretch into the distance. The whole scene was covered with a dusting of snow that had fallen the night before. The cold, crisp air swirled in vanishing mists as we breathed in the whole spectacular scene.

We'd come outside after several hours of conversation in which we'd talked about the research going on at the Institute and the foibles and pitfalls of cross-cultural exchange. We had already come to definite agreement on the importance and need for the kind of initiative that Tom was about to push forward at the Institute. Yes, it would be possible to find researchers in China who were receptive to the multi-disciplinary approach of SFI. Yes, we could help to focus the agenda for a meeting between Chinese and Western scientists so that each group could come to understand and appreciate the particular perspectives of the other.

"But, what I really want to know is," said Tom breaking a short silence as we rounded a bend in the path and stood watching the clouds scud across the sky overarching the peaks of the Sangre de Cristo Mountains, "what is *qì*?"

Tà Gē Tú (Beating Time) by Ma Yuan; Southern Song Dynasty.
In the collection of the Beijing Imperial Palace Museum.

Appendix 1: Heavenly Stems and Earthly Branches

Tiān Gān Dì Zhī

Heavenly Stems	Corresponding Phase	Corresponding Star
First Heavenly Stem (*jiă*)	Wood	Jupiter
Second Heavenly Stem (*yĭ*)		
Third Heavenly Stem (*bĭng*)	Fire	Mars
Fourth Heavenly Stem (*dīng*)		
Fifth Heavenly Stem (*wù*)	Earth	Saturn
Sixth Heavenly Stem (*jĭ*)		
Seventh Heavenly Stem (*gēng*)	Metal	Venus
Eighth Heavenly Stem (*xīn*)		
Ninth Heavenly Stem (*rén*)	Water	Mercury
Tenth Heavenly Stem (*guĭ*)		

Earthly Branch	Symbolic Animal	Corresponding Hours
First Earthly Branch (*zĭ*)	Rat	23:00 – 1:00
Second Earthly Branch (*chŏu*)	Ox	1:00 – 3:00
Third Earthly Branch (*yín*)	Tiger	3:00 – 5:00
Fourth Earthly Branch (*măo*)	Rabbit	5:00 – 7:00
Fifth Earthly Branch (*chén*)	Dragon	7:00 – 9:00
Sixth Earthly Branch (*sí*)	Snake	9:00 – 11:00
Seventh Earthly Branch (*wŭ*)	Horse	11:00 – 13:00
Eighth Earthly Branch (*wèi*)	Sheep	13:00 – 15:00
Ninth Earthly Branch (*shēn*)	Monkey	15:00 – 17:00
Tenth Earthly Branch (*yŏu*)	Rooster	17:00 – 19:00
Eleventh Earthly Branch (*xū*)	Dog	19:00 – 21:00
Twelfth Earthly Branch (*hài*)	Pig	21:00 – 23:00

Appendix 2: The Twenty-Four Seasonal Division Points

	Order and Name of Seasonal Division Point	Sun's Position at Ecliptic	Date on Gregorian Calendar
Spring	1. Beginning of Spring *(lì chūn)*	315°	February, 4th or 5th
	2. Rain Water *(yǔ shuǐ)*	330°	February, 19th or 20th
	3. Waking of Insects *(jīng zhé)*	345°	March, 5th or 6th
	4. Vernal Equinox *(chūn fēn)*	0°	March, 20th or 21st
	5. Pure Brightness *(qīng míng)*	15°	April, 5th or 6th
	6. Grain Rain *(gǔ yǔ)*	30°	April, 20th or 21st
Summer	7. Beginning of Summer *(lì xià)*	45°	May, 5th or 6th
	8. Grain Budding *(xiǎo mǎn)*	60°	May, 21st or 22nd
	9. Grain in Ear *(máng zhǒng)*	75°	June, 6th or 7th
	10. Summer Solstice *(xià zhì)*	90°	June, 21st or 22nd
	11. Slight Heat *(xiǎo shǔ)*	105°	July, 7th or 8th
	12. Great Heat *(dà shǔ)*	120°	July, 23rd or 24th
Autumn	13. Beginning of Autumn *(lì qīu)*	135°	August, 7th or 8th
	14. Limit of Heat *(chù shǔ)*	150°	August, 23rd or 24th
	15. White Dew *(bái lù)*	165°	September, 7th or 8th
	16. Autumnal Equinox *(qīu fēn)*	180°	September, 23rd or 24th
	17. Cold Dew *(hán lù)*	195°	October, 8th or 9th
	18. Frost's Descent *(shuāng jiàng)*	210°	October, 23rd or 24th
Winter	19. Beginning of Winter *(lì dōng)*	225°	November, 7th or 8th
	20. Slight Snow *(xiǎo xuě)*	240°	November, 22nd or 23rd
	21. Great Snow *(dà xuě)*	255°	December, 7th or 8th
	22. Winter Solstice *(dōng zhì)*	270°	December, 22nd or 23rd
	23. Slight Cold *(xiǎo hán)*	285°	January, 5th or 6th
	24. Great Cold *(dà hán)*	300°	January, 20th or 21st

Appendix 3: A Concise Chronology of Chinese History

Period of the Five Legendary Rulers c.2600 BC – 1600 BC		Huang Di	
		Zhuan Xu	
		Di Ku	
		Yao of Tang	
		Shun of Yu	
Xia Dynasty			c. 2100 BC – c.1600 BC
Shang Dynasty			c.1600 BC – c.1100 BC
Western Zhou Dynasty			c.1100 BC – c.771 BC
Eastern Zhou Dynasty 770 BC – 256 BC	Spring and Autumn Period		770 BC – 476 BC
	Warring States Period		475 BC – 221 BC
Qin Dynasty			221 BC –206 BC
Han Dynasty 206 BC – 220 AD	Western Han		206 BC – 25 AD
	Eastern Han		25 – 220
Three Kingdoms 220 – 280	Wei		220 – 265
	Shu Han		221 – 263
	Wu		222 – 280
Jin Dynasty 265 – 420	Western Jin		265 – 316
	Eastern Jin		317 – 420
Northern and Southern Dynasties 386 – 589	Southern Dynasties	Song	420 – 479
		Qi	479 – 502
		Liang	502 – 557
		Chen	557 – 589
	Northern Dynasties	Northern Wei	386 – 534
		Eastern Wei	534 – 550
		Northern Qi	550 – 577
		Western Wei	535 –556
		Northern Zhou	577 – 581
Sui Dynasty			581 – 618
Tang Dynasty			618 –907
Five Dynasties and Ten States	Five Dynasties 907 – 960	Later Liang	907 –923
		Later Tang	923 – 936
		Later Jin	936 – 946
		Later Han	947 – 950
		Later Zhou	951 – 960
	Ten States 902 - 979	Northern Han	951 – 979
		Wu	902 – 937
		Southern Tang	937 – 975
		Wu Yue	907 – 978
		Min	909 – 945
		Southern Han	917 – 971
		Chu	927 – 951
		Jing Nan (Nan Ping)	924 – 963
		Former Shu	907 – 925
		Later Shu	934 - 965
Song Dynasty 960 – 1279	Northern Song		960 –1127
	Southern Song		1127 – 1279
Liao (*or* Qi Dan, *or* Chi Tan)			916 – 1125
Jin			1115 –1234
Xi Xia (*or* Tangut)			1038 – 1227
Yuan Dynasty			1279 – 1368 (est. 1206)
Ming Dynasty			1368 – 1644
Qing Dynasty			1644 – 1911 (est. 1616)
Republic of China			1912 – 1949
People's Republic of China			1949 –

Bibliography

Ames, Roger, Trans. *Sun-Tzu The Art of War*. New York: Ballantine Books, 1993.

Beijing Planetarium. *Zhōng Guǒ Gǔ Dài Tiān Wén Xué Chéng Jìu (Achievements of Chinese Ancient Astronomy)*. Beijing: Beijing Science and Technology Press, 1987.

Chen Jun Ying. *Shī Jīng Yì Zhù (Translation and Annotation of Shī Jīng)*. Shanghai: Shanghai Ancient Literature Press, 1985.

Cheng Su Tang. *Zi Wǔ Lú Zhù Shuō Ào (Explanations of the Mystery of the Streaming and Flowing of the First and Seventh Earthly Branches)*. Beijing: People's Health Press, 1991.

Du Xian Chen. *Nèi Dān Tàn Mì (Exploration of the Secrets of Internal Elixir)*. Beijing: Ancient Literature Press, 1994.

Hàn Yǔ Dà Zì Diǎn (Great Dictionary of Chinese Characters). Sichuan Lexicon Press and Hubei Lexicon Press, 1986

Hao Qin. *Dǎo Yǐn Yǎng Shēng (Dǎo Yǐn and Yǎng Shēng)*. Sichuan: Bā Shǔ Books, 1995.

Kong Jian Min. *Zhōng Guó Yī Xué Shǐ Gāng (Outline of the History of Chinese Medicine)*. Beijing: People's Health Press, 1998.

Lau, D.C., Ames, R. *Yuan Dao*. NewYork: Ballantine Books, 1998.

Ledderose, Lothar. *Ten Thousand Things*. Princeton: Princeton University Press, 2000.

Lin Yu Tang. *My Country, My People*. New York: John Day Company, 1936.

Liu Zhi Cheng. *Hàn Zì Yǔ Huá Xià Wén Huà (Chinese Characters and Chinese Culture)*. Sichuan: Bā Shǔ Books, 1995.

Lo, Benjamin, and Inn, Martin. *Cheng Tzu's Thirteen Treatises on T'ai Ch'i Ch'uan*. Berkeley: North Atlantic Books, 1985.

_____. *The Essence of T'ai Ch'i Ch'uan*. Berkely, CA: North Atlantic Books, 1985

Ma Bo Ying. *Zhōng Guó Yī Xué Wén Huà Shǐ (Cultural History of Chinese Medicine)*. Shanghai: Shanghai People's Press, 1994.

Needham, Joseph. *Science and Civilization in China, Vol 2*. Cambridge: Oxford University Press, 1956.

Roth, Harold. *Original Tao*. New York. Columbia University Press. 1999.

Sichuan Antiques Committee. *Sichuan Wén Wù (Sichuan Antiques)*. Sichuan: Sichuan Provincial Antique Management Committee.

Sun Si Mao. *Qiān Jīn Fāng (Prescriptions Worth a Thousand Pieces of Gold)*. Ed. Liu Geng Sheng *et al.* Beijing: Huá Xià Press, 1993.

Teng, Xin Cai, and Teng, Yong. *Guǎn Zǐ Bái Huà Jīn Yì (Guǎn Zǐ Translation in Modern Chinese)* Beijing: Chinese Book Store, 1994.

Teng, Xiu Zhan, *et al. Liè Xiān Quán Zhuàn Shēn Xiān Zhuàn Zhù Yì (Annotation of Liè Xiān Zhuàn Shén Xiān Zhuàn)*. Tianjing: Bái Huā Literature and Art Press, 1996.

Unschuld, Paul. *Medicine in China: A History of Ideas*. Berkeley: University of California Press, 1988.

Wei Qi Peng, and Hu Xiang Hua. *Mǎ Wāng Duī Hàn Mù Yī Shū Jiào Shì (Proofing and Annotation of the Medical Texts from Mǎ Wáng Tuī Han Tomb Cave)*. Sichuan: Chengdu Press, 1992.

Wiseman N., and Feng, Ye. *A Practical Dictionary of Chinese Medicine*. Brookline, MA: Paradigm Publications. 1998.

Xie, Xiang Hao, and Liu, Zong Xian. *Zhōng Guó Rú Xué (Chinese Confucianism)*. Sichuan: Sichuan People's Press, 1993.

Yang Rong Guo. *Jiǎn Mín Zhōng Guó Zhé Xué Shǐ (Practical and Concise History of Chinese Philosophy)*. Beijing: People's Health Press, 1973.

Zhang Li Wen. *Qì*. Beijing: China People's University Press, 1990.

Zhou Xue Xi. *Yì Xué Shí Jiǎng (Ten Lectures on the Study of Yì)*. Sichuan: Sichuan Science and Technology Press, 1986.

Zu Bao Quan. *Wén Xīn Diāo Lóng Jiě Shuō (Explanations and Annotations of Wēn Xīng Diāo Lóng)*. Anhui: Anhui Education Press, 1993.

Index